APPLYING SKILLS FOR FOUNDATION GCSE 1–5 MATHS EXAMS

Michael White

Elmwood Education

First published 2017 by
Elmwood Education Limited
Unit 5 Mallow Park
Watchmead
Welwyn Garden City
Herts. AL7 1GX
Tel. 01707 333232

ISBN 9781 906 622 640

Typeset and illustrated by Tech-Set Ltd., Gateshead, Tyne and Wear.

PREFACE

This stand-alone book provides banks of questions which have been written to complement any GCSE resources.

The questions focus on assessment objectives AO2 and AO3, ie. reasoning, interpreting, communicating and solving non-routine problems.

There are 41 sets of questions which can be used throughout the GCSE course or as more of a revisional aid. They may be tackled initially by groups of students to explore and discuss strategies or worked at individually.

25 sets of questions focus on grades 1–3 material but are often more challenging because of the AO2 and AO3 focus. The remaining 16 sets of questions focus on grades 4–5 topics (these are referenced by EXT in the section headings). Some sections are specific to Number, Algebra, Geometry or Statistics only. Ratio and proportion run throughout these.

Users of the main Elmwood Education Foundation GCSE Maths 1–3 and 4–5 textbooks will find links to these books in the answer section.

Students find the kind of questions in this book very demanding. The author has tried to provide a reasonable spread of complexity within each unit. Many schools have used units in Part One on a fortnightly basis in Year 10 then units in Part Two on a fortnightly basis in Year 11.

The author is indebted to Jonathan Stevens for his invaluable contribution to this book.

Michael White

CONTENTS LIST

PART ONE

1   Kayla says the answer to $7 + 3 \times 2$ is 20.
    Alex says that Kayla is wrong.
    Explain clearly why Alex thinks that the answer is not 20.

2   Kate saves £7 each week for 18 weeks. Her grandparents give her £50 for her
    birthday. Kate wants to buy a camera which costs £225.

    (a) Can Kate afford to buy the camera?

    (b) If yes, how much money does she have left over?
         If no, how much more money does she need to save?

3   There is a major fire in Victoria in Australia.
    Planes are used to drop water on the fire.
    Plane A and plane B both leave their base
    at 08:00.

    Plane A returns to base every 50 minutes
    for more water.

    Plane B returns to base every 70 minutes
    for more water.

    At what time will both planes next be back at their base together?

4   The number of people at a football match is 64 000. This number has been
    rounded off to the nearest 1000.

    Write down the least number of people who might really have been at the
    football match.

5   Two clubs put on firework displays.

    The Greenbank club sell 900 tickets at £6 each.

    They spend £2600 on the fireworks.

    Morley rugby club sell 1250 tickets at £8 each.
    The cost of their fireworks is £5900.

    Which club makes the most profit and by how much?

6
Mableford −6°C	Cannington 7°C
Melton −9°C	
Heston −2°C	Welby ?

The difference between the temperatures at Melton and Cannington is the same as the difference between the temperatures at Heston and Welby.

Write down the **two** possible temperatures at Welby.

> **Hint:**
> The *difference* between 10 and 6 is 10 − 6 = 4.

7   Colin and Alisha need to make a factor tree for the number 60.
    They each begin as shown below:

Colin
60
6   10

Alisha
60
2   30

    (a) *Explain fully* whether it matters which numbers they use first.

    (b) Write down 60 as a product of its prime factors.

8   Katya hires a car. The cost is worked out by the formula below:

| cost = fixed charge + cost per mile × number of miles |

Hint:
Subtract the
fixed charge
from the cost
to begin with.

The fixed charge is £65. The cost per mile is 20p.
How many miles did Katya travel if the cost of
hiring the car was £125?

9   Mrs Thomas needs help at home. A nurse visits every 6 days and a social
worker visits every 8 days. The nurse and social worker both visit on July 19th.
On what date will both the nurse and social worker next visit Mrs Thomas on
the same day?

10 Owen and Stella have always wanted to
visit the Grand Canyon in the USA.
They decide to save together for a
holiday for two in the USA which
will cost a total of £6100.

Owen's take-home pay each month is
£1463. He shares a flat. The table *below*
shows what he has to pay out each month.
He saves the rest of his money.

Rent	£328
Electricity	£22
Gas	£18
Water	£13
Phone	£40
Council tax	£25
Food/entertainment	£400

Stella lives at home with her parents. Her take-home pay each month is £1220.
Each month she gives her parents £400, pays £35 for her phone and spends
£160 on entertainment. She saves the rest of her money.

How many months will it take Owen and Stella to save enough money for the
USA holiday?

11 Does $(-2)^3$ equal -8 or 8? *Give full reasons* for your answer.

12 Food is served from a barbecue at a school fete.
    The prices of the food and drink are shown below.

burger	£1.90	coke	80p
sausage	90p	lemonade	70p
kebab	£2.15	juice	75p
chicken	£1.85	water	70p
steak	£3.10		

(a) Gabrielle and her three friends turn up with a £10 note.
    All the sausages have been sold. Have Gabrielle and her friends got enough
    money for each of them to have one item of food and one drink?
    Explain your reasons fully.

(b) They actually borrow some money from Gabrielle's mother and buy two
    kebabs, two steaks, three cokes and one water. What is the least amount of
    money they borrow from Gabrielle's mother?

N   NUMBER 1B

1   m, n and p are *different* prime numbers.
Find possible values for m, n and p such that

$$m + 3n = p$$

Hint:
A prime number has two factors only, 1 and itself.

2
Ben and Louise each have a market stall.

Ben buys 150 sunglasses for £900 and sells them all at £8 each. Louise buys 120 sunglasses for £600 and sells 110 of them at £9 each. Who makes the larger profit and by how much?

3   Mia wants to plant 144 trees in rows.
She wants the number of trees in each row to equal the number of rows.

(a) Explain or draw how she would place the trees.

(b) Mia changes her mind. She now decides the number of rows should be four times greater than the number of trees in each row.
Explain or draw how she would now place the trees.

4   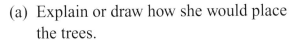 The numbers 6 and 8 give the same product as the numbers 3, 4 and n.
Find the value of n.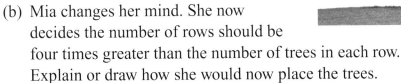

Hint:
The product of numbers is found by multiplying the numbers together.

5   A factory is protected by two guards.

   Guard 1 leaves the main office and returns to the office every 15 minutes.

   Guard 2 leaves the main office and returns to the office every 18 minutes.

   If both guards leave the main office at 10 p.m., when will they next be back at the office at the same time?

6   Nathan and his friends sell raffle tickets to raise money for charity. Each ticket costs 50p.

   They raise £621 when the raffle is made and they have paid for the prizes shown below.

Balloon ride for two	£90
Restaurant meal for two	£50
Two local theatre tickets	£32
Bottle of Bordeaux wine	£15

   How many raffle tickets did Nathan and his friends sell in total?

7   Harry uses a calculator to work out the square of -8.

   He types in -8^2 and gets the answer -64.

   His teacher tells him he has the wrong answer.

   (a) What should the answer be?

   (b) How should Harry have typed this question into his calculator?

8   One day Max sells 20 bacon sandwiches in his cafe for £3.50 each.

   For each sandwich he uses 2 slices of bread, 2 rashers of bacon and a small amount of margarine.

   The cost of the bread and bacon is shown opposite. In total the margarine and electricity used to make the 20 bacon sandwiches is £3.50.

Cost price
Loaf of bread £1.20 (20 slices)
Pack of bacon £1.99 (8 rashers)

   How much profit did Max make on the bacon sandwiches?

9 Matt goes into college on 4 days of each week. His mother gives him £20 each week to buy his lunches. His lunch costs him £4 each day.

He saves the money left over each week throughout the year (term time only: 38 weeks). How much money does he save in total?

10 Tamsin draws a factor tree to express 96 as the product of its prime factors.
She decides that $96 = 2 \times 2 \times 4 \times 7$ but has made some mistakes in her tree.

(a) Describe the mistakes she has made in her tree.

(b) Draw a correct factor tree.

(c) Express 96 as the product of its prime factors.

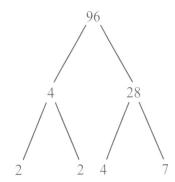

11

Jack's freezer is usually at a temperature of −25°C. Jack goes to bed at 10 p.m. and comes down to the kitchen in the morning at 7 a.m.
The freezer breaks down at 11 p.m.
The temperature rises 4°C each hour.
The food in the freezer will be ruined if the temperature goes above 0°C for more than two hours.

Jack checks the freezer as soon as he comes down to the kitchen in the morning. Is the food in the freezer still OK or is it ruined?

Give reasons for your answer.

12 A group of 10 people do the National Lottery. Six more people join the group. After a few weeks, the group win £33 600. The money is shared out equally between the people in the group.

One of these people decides to share out his winnings equally between his wife, himself and his three children.

His youngest child spends £93 on computer games. How much money does this child have left over from the winnings?

N | NUMBER 1EXT

1 Asha changes 625000 into a standard form number. She says that it is 6.25×10^3.
Jason works out 6.25×10^3 on a calculator and gets the answer 6250 which is
not the number Asha started with.

(a) Describe what mistake you think
Asha made when she tried to
change 625000 into standard form.

(b) Write 625000 in standard form.

> **Hint:**
> A standard form number is
> written in the form $A \times 10^n$
> where $1 \leqslant A < 10$ and n is an
> integer (whole number).

2 The distances (in km) between several towns is shown below.

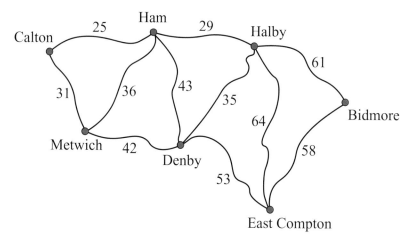

All the towns need to be connected to each other by a TV cable.
Copy the diagram then work out the least amount of TV cable that would be
needed. Explain your answer fully.

3 In computing, 1 megabyte $= 10^6$ bytes and 1 gigabyte $= 10^9$ bytes.

How many megabytes in 4 gigabytes?

4 Milena sells candles at a market stall.

One day she buys 45 boxes at £2.50 each.
There are 16 candles in each box.

She sells a box of candles for £3.50 or
she sells individual candles at 60p each.

By the end of the day she has sold 35 boxes.
She sells all the other candles individually
but has 15 candles left over.

How much profit does Milena make on the candles?

5 Mrs Reece organizes a year 11 trip to the theatre to see a play for their GCSE
English. The costs are shown below:

ticket	£12.50 (buy 9 tickets and get one extra ticket free)
coach (52 seats)	£325
other costs	£35

Each student has to pay £19.

90 students go on the trip.

(a) How much money is left over when all the costs have been paid?

(b) At the last minute the theatre removes its free ticket offer.
    Is there still enough money to cover the costs?
    If not, how much more money is needed?

6 $m = 2 \times 3^2 \times 7$ and $n = 2^3 \times 3 \times 5$

Work out the lowest common multiple of the numbers m and n.

7   A factory worker works on an assembly line
    making magnifying glasses.

    She gets £40 each day plus £5 for every 200
    magnifying glasses she deals with.
    One week she works for five days and deals
    with 1200 magnifying glasses.
    How much does she earn?

8   Teresa works at a small primary school. On her birthday she wants to give out
    slices of birthday cake. She needs plates and forks.

    Her local store sells paper plates in boxes of fifteen at £1.99 each and packs of
    forty plastic forks at £2.20 each.

    Teresa buys exactly the same number of plates and forks. Assuming she buys
    the least amount to satisfy this statement, how much does Teresa spend in
    total?

9   There are 6.3×10^5 new computers made
    each month.

    During the same time period 2.8×10^4 old
    computers are destroyed.

    Calculate the increase in the number of
    computers over a five year period.

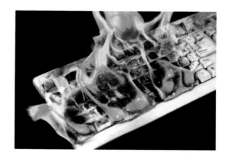

10   Mark writes:

$$3^0 \div 3^2 = 3^{0-2} = 3^{-2}$$

$$\text{so } 3^{-2} = 3^0 \div 3^2 = \frac{3^0}{3^2}$$

$$\text{so } 3^{-2} = \frac{1}{3^2}$$

$$\text{so } 3^{-2} = \frac{1}{9}$$

Hint:

$$a^2 \div a^2 = a^{2-2} = a^0$$

$$\text{so } a^0 = a^2 \div a^2 = 1$$

$$\text{so } a^0 = 1$$

Do the same as Mark above starting with $4^0 \div 4^3$ and follow the stages to work out the value of 4^{-3}.

11   The Venn diagram opposite is used to find the Highest Common Factor of two numbers A and B.

The Highest Common Factor is 28.

Write down the values of the two numbers A and B.

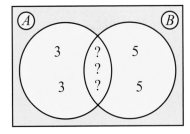

12 The Howell family are going on a ski holiday.
They need to hire skis and jackets and must also buy
ski passes.
The prices in three resort shops are shown below.

Shop A	
Ski hire	€15 per day
Ski hire (under 16)	€12 per day
jacket	€3.50 per day
ski pass	€20 per day
or	€35 for every 2 days

Shop B	
Ski hire	€90 per week
Ski hire (under 16)	€70 per week
jacket	€26 per week
ski pass	€130 per week

Shop C	
Ski hire	€18 per day
or	€44 for every 3 days
Ski hire (under 16)	€12 per day
or	€30 for every 3 days
jacket	€3.50 per day
or	€10 for every 3 days
ski pass	€20 per day
or	€56 for every 3 days

Mr and Mrs Howell have
two children, aged 9 and 12.

Explain the cheapest way
in which the Howell family
can all hire skis, a jacket
and buy a ski pass for a
seven day holiday.

Give the total number of
euros they must spend.

A   ALGEBRA 1A

1   The expression $3x + 6y + x - 2 - 3y + 1$ is simplified.
Which answer below is correct?

| $3x + 3y - 3$ | $3x + 3y - 1$ | $4x + 3y - 1$ |

2   Milena finds the value of $3a^2$ when $a = 2$.
She writes down the answer 36.

(a) This is incorrect. Explain what mistake she has made.

(b) Work out the correct answer.

3

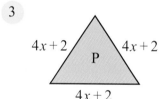
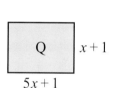
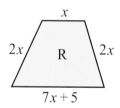

Which of the shapes above has the largest perimeter?
Explain your answer fully.

4   Aidan expands the following brackets:

| $2(8a + 4)$ | $4(4a + 3)$ | $8(2a + 1)$ |
| P | Q | R |

Hint:
'Expand' means
'multiply out'.

Which question above gives a different answer to
the other two questions? Show all answers clearly.

5 Prove that $\dfrac{n^2 \times (n^3)^3}{n^6}$ is identical

to $\dfrac{(n^2)^5}{n^2 \times n^3}$

Hint:
Simplify both expressions to show that they are identical (exactly the same as each other).

6 A red suitcase costs £42.
A blue suitcase costs £39.

(a) Write down an expression for how much money it costs to buy x red suitcases.

(b) Write down an expression for how much more money it costs to buy x red suitcases than to buy x blue suitcases.

7 If $\dfrac{n}{6} = 9$ then $n = 15$.

(a) Explain clearly why n cannot equal 15.

(b) Solve $\dfrac{n}{6} = 9$

8 A young zebra weighs $(5a + 7b)$ kg.

During the following week it loses $(a + b)$ kg of its weight.

In the week after that it gains $(2a + 3b)$ kg in weight.

Write down an expression for what the zebra now weighs.

9   A box holds $(7x + 2)$ packets of crisps when full.

   (a) Write down and simplify an expression for how many packets of crisps are held in 4 full boxes.

   (b) How many packets of crisps are in 4 full boxes when $x = 6$?

10   An exam question worth 2 marks is 'factorise $4x^2 + 6xy$'.
   Tom writes the answer $2x(2x + 3y)$.
   Eva writes the answer $x(4x + 6y)$.
   One person only scores 1 mark and the other person scores 2 marks.

   (a) Who scores only 1 mark?

   (b) Explain clearly why this person has lost 1 mark.

11   A restaurant has a special price for more than 10 guests given by the formula below:

   Price = fixed charge + £13 × number of guests

   Calculate the number of guests if the fixed charge was £55 and the guests paid a total of £315.

12

$n + 2$

$5n + 1$

The triangle shown above is equilateral.
The perimeter of the rectangle is the same length as the perimeter of the triangle.
Find an expression, in terms of n, for the length of one side of the equilateral triangle.

A ALGEBRA 1EXT

1 The perimeter of the rectangular room shown opposite is 36 m.

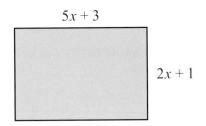

$5x + 3$

$2x + 1$

(a) Form an equation, in terms of x.

(b) Solve the equation to find the value of x.

(c) Find the actual area of this room (in m^2).

2 Carson solves an equation as follows:

$$6n - 4 = 2n + 16$$

(Subtract $2n$ from both sides)

$$4n - 4 = 16$$

Subtract 4 from both sides

$$4n = 12$$

$$n = \frac{12}{4} = 3$$

Carson checks whether $n = 3$ fits the equation. He finds that it does not.

(a) Explain clearly what mistake Carson made.

(b) Find the correct value of n.

3 Anna has x coloured pencils. Charles has four times as many pencils as Anna.

Bailey has 3 more pencils than Charles.

They have a total of 30 pencils. How many pencils does Bailey have?

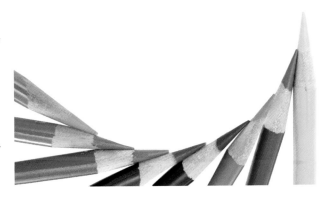

4   The cost C of hiring a tile cutting machine is given by the formula

$$C = 23 + 15n$$

where n is the number of days of hire. How much more does it cost to hire the machine for 9 days compared to 4 days?

5

$n + 3$

$n + 4$

Multiply the sides of this rectangle together to find an expression for its area.

Hint:
Remember FOIL to expand two brackets.
First terms
Outer terms
Inner terms
Last terms

6   A cookbook gives the rule below for roasting a joint of beef.

$$T = 25W + 30$$

where T is the cooking time in minutes and W is the weight of the beef.

(a) Dylan has a 2.5 kg joint of beef. If he starts cooking it at 11:30 a.m., will it be ready to eat by 12:45 p.m.? Explain your reasons.

(b) Ava has a joint of beef which takes 1 hour 45 minutes to cook. Work out the weight of this joint of beef.

7   Three friends have a total of 23 euro coins. Max has x coins.

Zoe has twice as many coins as Max.

Lily has 5 coins less than Max.
How many coins does Lily have?

8　Rebecca solves an equation as follows:

$$2(3x - 4) = 28$$
$$6x - 8 = 28$$
$$6x = 36$$
$$x = 6$$

Has Rebecca made any mistakes.
Describe the mistakes if she has made any.

9

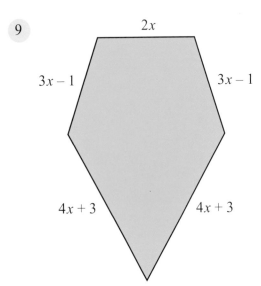

The perimeter of this pentagon is 52 cm.

What is the actual length of the longest side of this pentagon?

Give your answer in cm.

10　Chloe, Jose and Ashna play games of pool against each other.

Chloe pots x balls.

Jose pots twice as many balls as Chloe.

Ashna pots six more balls than Chloe.

They pot a total of 74 balls.

How many balls did Chloe pot?

11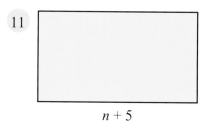

n + 5

An expression for the area of this rectangle is $n^2 + 3n - 10$.
Find an expression for the width of this rectangle by factorising.

12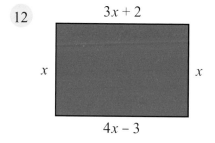

3x + 2

x   x

4x − 3

Work out the actual perimeter of this rectangle. All measurements are given in cm.

Hint:
Opposite sides of a rectangle are equal.
Use them to form an equation.

M | MIXED 1A

1 Callum and Emma work out the value of $-4 - (-4)$
Callum says that $-4 - (-4) = -4 + 4 = -8$
Emma says that $-4 - (-4) = -4 + 4 = 0$
Who is correct? Give reasons for your answer.

Hint:
Use a number line to explain your answer.

2 Three friends go to the theatre to watch a show.
The prices are shown below.

Ticket £22.50 per person
Booking Fee £2.75 per person
Cloakroom £1.50 per item

How much does it cost all 3 friends in total
to go to the show if two of them each leave
a coat in the cloakroom?

3 In a park there are 10 rabbits at the start of February.
Each month the number of rabbits doubles.
At the start of which month will the number of rabbits first be greater than 200?

4 Prove that

$$3n + 10 + 5n - 6 + 11 - 2n \equiv 3(2n + 5)$$

Hint:
'$\equiv$' means 'is identical to'.
Simplify both sides to show that they are the same.

5   The chart shows the shortest distances, in miles, between pairs of cities.
For example, the shortest distance between Leeds and Manchester is 44 miles.

Leeds				
190	London			
44	188	Manchester		
212	112	194	Bristol	
139	97	112	82	Birmingham

Sarah sells for a company. She can claim travel expenses of 22p per mile and she can claim expenses for meals. She lives in Manchester. On one journey she travels by car to Bristol then London then back to Manchester.
She claims for meals costing a total of £33.25 and for the travel expenses.

If Sarah spent a total of £97.47 of her own money on the petrol and meals, what profit does she make from the expenses?

6

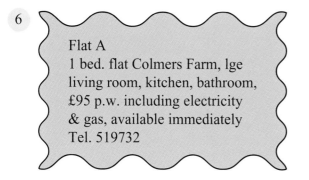

Flat A
1 bed. flat Colmers Farm, lge living room, kitchen, bathroom, £95 p.w. including electricity & gas, available immediately
Tel. 519732

Allison is looking for a flat.
She finds the details of two flats.

Flat B
1 bed. flat Saint Agnes, living room/kitchen combined, £88 p.w. plus electricity/gas to pay, shared garden Tel. 678913

For flat A, Allison would need to take two buses (each costing 80p) to get to work and the same to get home again.
For flat B, Allison can get to work on one bus only costing 70p and the same to get home again.

Allison works from Monday to Friday each week. The average cost of electricity would be £6.30 a week. The weekly average cost of gas would be £5.50. By considering the rent, electricity, gas and bus travel, which flat would be cheaper for Allison to take and by how much per week?

7 Three expressions are given below.

$a(a + 6)$ $a^2 - 9$ $5a - 2$

    P   Q   R

(a) Which expression has the greatest value when $a = 3$?
Show all your working out.

(b) Which expression has the greatest value when $a = -3$?
Show all your working out.

8 Hayley makes four window frames for a new house.
For each window frame she needs three pieces of
wood which are 1.2 m long and three pieces of
wood which are 1 m long.

The wood is delivered to Hayley in lengths of 3.5 m.

What is the least number of 3.5 m lengths of wood that
Hayley will have to cut to make her four window frames?
Explain fully how she would get the pieces of wood that she needs.

9 Tanya is helping out on a farm picking cabbages.
Her wage, W, for the day is given by the formula

$$W = 12n + 15$$

where n is the number of boxes of cabbages which she fills.

How many boxes did she fill if her wage for the day was £63?

10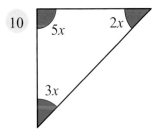

Work out the size of the smallest angle in this triangle.

11 $17 \times 19 = 323$ Use this information to find the lowest common multiple of 51 and 19.

12

SUNSHINE SHACK

Soup of the day	£1.90
Pasty	£1.40
Toasted sandwich	£1.60
Salad	£1.50
Tea	80p
Coffee	90p
Juice	80p
Cola	70p

10% off all prices before 11 a.m.

Andrea and Claire arrive at the Sunshine Shack at 9:45 a.m. Andrea has soup and a cup of coffee. Claire has a toasted sandwich, a salad and a cup of tea.

Andrea pays for everything with a £10 note and leaves a £1 tip.
How much money does Andrea have left over from the £10 note?

1

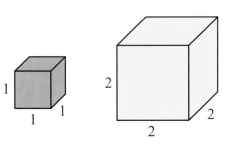 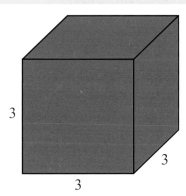

All units above are in cm.

The volumes of each cube are written below:

$$1 \times 1 \times 1 = 1 \, cm^3$$

$$2 \times 2 \times 2 = 8 \, cm^3$$

$$3 \times 3 \times 3 = 27 \, cm^3$$

The side lengths continue to increase by 1 cm at a time.
Work out the side length which gives the largest volume which is smaller than 750 cm³.

2 Grace says that $n^2 + n^2 + n^2 = n^6$
Misha says that Grace has mixed up her rules.

(a) How would the question need to change in order to give the answer n^6?

(b) Simplify $n^2 + n^2 + n^2$

3 A school can buy boxes of pritt stick glue in two sizes.
A small box contains x sticks. A large box contains y sticks.

(a) The school buys 6 large boxes and 2 small boxes.
Write down an expression for the total number of
sticks the school buys.

(b) The school uses up $(2x + y)$ sticks. Write down an expression
for the number of sticks remaining.

(c) When the school bought 6 large boxes and 2 small boxes,
it had a total of 170 sticks. How many sticks might there
have been in each type of box?

4 Li needs to put brackets into the calculation $3 \times 6 - 2 + 4$ to get the answer 16.
He decides on $3 \times 6 - (2 + 4)$.
Is he correct? If not, where should the brackets be placed?

5 In a TV game show, each player is given
25 points to start with. Each player scores
4 more points when a question is answered
correctly. The total number of points T is
given by the formula

$$T = 25 + 4n$$

where n is the number of correct answers
given.

If Tristan scores 61 points in total, how many
correct answers did he give?

> **Hint:**
> Replace T with 61 in the formula
> then solve the equation.

6 Jess says that if she takes any positive whole number, adds 9 then doubles the
answer, she will always get an *even* number.
Explain clearly why Jess would indeed always get an *even* number.

7 Lucy needs to hire a car for 3 months (13 weeks).

> 'Autohire' charge a fixed cost of £85 plus £21 for each day.

> 'Carmark' charge a fixed cost of £420 plus £118 for each week.

Which firm will be cheaper and by how much?

8 (a) Expand and simplify $2(3n + 5) + 4(5n - 2)$

(b) Factorise your answer to part (a), i.e. take out the common factor.

9 Mason, Alyssa and Rahul are training on the running track at their local athletics club.

Mason	9 minutes
Alyssa	8 minutes
Rahul	6 minutes

The table shows how long they each take to complete one lap of the track.

They leave the start line at the same time and run for 90 minutes in total. When they are next all at the start line at **the same time**, how much longer do they run for before completing the 90 minutes?

10 Alexa and 3 friends need to book their summer holiday.
They plan to share two twin rooms at the Regala hotel.
The cost of the rooms is shown below.

	6th June–3rd July		4th July–7th August		8th August–12th September		13th September–15th October	
	7 nights	14 nights	7 nights	14 nights	7 nights	14 nights	7 nights	14 nights
Single room	£525	£675	£595	£765	£625	£780	£575	£720
Double room	£605	£775	£675	£865	£705	£880	£645	£800
Twin room	£605	£785	£685	£880	£715	£895	£645	£810

Each price shown above is the price per person. Alexa and her friends wish to go on 15th August for 14 nights.

Alexa pays a deposit of £245.
She has 5 months to save the rest of the money. How much money does she need to save each month to be able to pay for this holiday?

11 (a) Expand $4(2x - 7)$

(b) Expand $4x(2x - 7)$

(c) Expand $x^2(2x^2 - 7)$

Hint:
$x^m \times x^n = x^{m+n}$

12 Bread rolls are sold in packs as shown below.

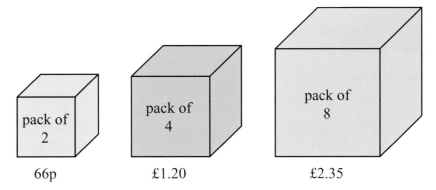

pack of 2

66p

pack of 4

£1.20

pack of 8

£2.35

Mrs Ryall has to make rolls for a party on Friday then for another party on Saturday. The bread rolls do not stay fresh overnight so she can only buy them on the day of the party.

Describe the cheapest way of buying the bread rolls if she needs 39 on the Friday and 29 on the Saturday.

1 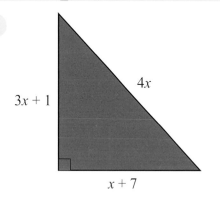 The perimeter of this triangle is 48 cm.

Work out the actual area of the triangle in cm².

4x

3x + 1

x + 7

2   $x^2 - 6x + 8 = (x - 2)(x + 4)$

Is the statement above true or false?
You must give clear reasons for your answer.

3   (a) Work out $\dfrac{1}{16} \times \dfrac{1}{3}$

Hint:

$a^{-n} = \dfrac{1}{a^n}$

   (b) Work out $4^{-2} \times 3^{-1}$

   (c) Which answer above is larger – (a) or (b)?

4   Proxima Centauri is the closest star to our Sun.

It is 39 840 000 000 000 000 metres away from the Earth.

Light travels at a speed of 3×10^8 m/s.

How many years does it take light to travel from Proxima Centauri to the Earth?

Give your answer to one decimal place.

Hint:

$\text{speed} = \dfrac{\text{distance}}{\text{time}}$

5   Mrs Collins needs to make a pack lunch for each of 60 children in her school. She will include 2 bread rolls and one packet of crisps in each pack lunch.

Packets of crisps come in large packs of 8.

Bread rolls come in packs of 12.

Mrs Collins uses the least number of packs of everything.

How many bread rolls and packets of crisps will she have left over when she has made all the lunches?

6   Hayden and Olivia solve an equation as shown below:

Hayden's answer   *Olivia's answer*

$\frac{n}{4} - 5 = 4$ $\frac{n}{4} - 5 = 4$

$n - 5 = 16$ $\frac{n}{4} = 9$

$n = 21$ $n = 36$

(a) Who is correct?

(b) Describe clearly what mistake was made by the other person.

(c) How can you check most easily if one of the answers above is correct?

7

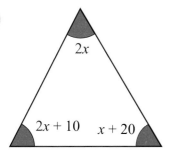

Find the value of x then write down the actual size of each angle in this triangle.

8   What number (*given in standard form*) needs to be subtracted from 400.4 to give 400.39?

9

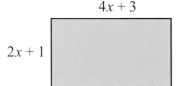

The perimeter of this rectangle is 80 cm.
Work out the actual area of this rectangle in cm².

10 $520 = 2^3 \times 5 \times 13$. Polly says that the lowest common multiple of 520 and 210 is 10920. Is Polly correct? If not, what is the lowest common multiple of 520 and 210?

11 Sophia likes to talk a lot! She decides to do a sponsored 'silence' to raise money for charity. Her sponsor form is shown below. She manages to stay silent for 14 hours.

She wants to raise £100.
Does she succeed?
Explain your reasons.

Name	Amount
Megan	50p per hour
Jane	25p per hour
Mum	£20
Aditi	£5
Kimberly	10p per hour
Dad	£20
Jason	50p per hour for the first 10 hours only
Mr Reed	£5
Auntie Molly	30p per hour for the first 12 hours then 60p per hour
Kevin	10p per hour
Sabina	£1
Shui	£1
Ian	£5 for the first 10 hours then an extra 20% if more than 10 hours
Mrs Cole	10p per hour
Aida	£1 for every complete 3 hours
Mrs Weaver	£2
Zoe	20p per hour
Amelia	25p per hour for the first 8 hours only
Ayden	£5
Mr Henry	40p per hour for the first 6 hours then 80p per hour

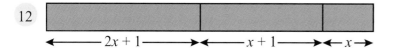

12

A piece of wood is 3 metres long.

It is cut into three parts as shown above.

The last part is x metres long. What fraction of the whole piece of wood is this last part?

N	NUMBER 2A

1   (a) How many thirds make a whole unit?

(b) How many thirds make 8 units?

(c) Work out $8 \div \frac{1}{3}$

Explain clearly your method.

(d) Work out $12 \div \frac{1}{3}$

2   Two groups of people were asked what they were most frightened of. The findings are shown below.

GROUP A	40 people
$\frac{1}{5}$ of the people said 'spiders'	
$\frac{3}{8}$ of the people said 'rats'	
The other people said 'closed spaces'	

GROUP B	72 people
$\frac{1}{3}$ of the people said 'heights'	
$\frac{2}{9}$ of the people said 'rats'	
$\frac{1}{6}$ of the people said 'closed spaces'	
The other people said 'spiders'	

Find the total number of people from both groups who said that they were most frightened of closed spaces.

3   Paige has a piece of ribbon. She uses $\frac{2}{5}$ of the ribbon on a present for her mother and another $\frac{1}{3}$ of the ribbon on a gift for her sister. She needs another 55 cm of ribbon for a final present.

Does she have enough ribbon left for this final present if she started with 240 cm of ribbon?

4 Finn says that '$\frac{3}{5} > 0.4$'

Is Finn correct?
You must show full working out to explain your answer.

5

Flavour	Number put on shelf	Number left on shelf
Plain	110	42
Cheese and onion	130	24
Roast chicken	60	9

The manager of a garage is given a target that each week the garage must sell at least $\frac{2}{3}$ of the packets of crisps which are put on the shelf.

The table above shows how many packets of crisps were put on the shelf during one week and how many were not sold.

Hint:
Add up the total number of packets of crisps put on the shelf first.

Did the garage meet the target? Explain your answer fully.

6 Amber needs to work out $\frac{1}{3} + \frac{1}{4}$

Copy and use the diagrams below to explain *why* the answer is $\frac{7}{12}$.

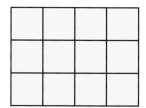

7 During his career, Ryan wins 48 Formula One races, $\frac{2}{3}$ of these races are in Europe. Out of these, $\frac{5}{8}$ were during the last 5 years of his career.

How many Formula One races in Europe did Ryan win during the last 5 years of his career?

8   Layla spends $\frac{2}{3}$ of her time sleeping and working.

She spends $\frac{1}{8}$ of her time on cooking and housework.

The rest of her time is spent on leisure.

What fraction of her time does Layla spend on leisure?

9

Brianna makes cakes for a tea shop. She uses $\frac{2}{5}$ kg of sugar for each cake. Brianna buys the sugar in 5 kg bags.

How many cakes can Brianna make with the sugar from one 5 kg bag?

Hint:
Work out $5 \div \frac{2}{5}$
or write $5 = \frac{25}{5}$
then work out how many $\frac{2}{5}$'s are needed to make $\frac{25}{5}$?

10 Marshall puts four decimals in order of size, starting with the smallest as shown below.

0.06   0.062   0.6   0.602

Is Marshall correct or not? Explain clearly how you checked the order of Marshall's numbers.

11 There are 72 flags flying outside a large building.
$\frac{5}{8}$ of these flags have blue in them.

Of these, $\frac{2}{3}$ also have red in them.

Of these, $\frac{1}{5}$ have green and $\frac{1}{2}$ have white.

How many flags in total contain blue, red, green
or blue, red, white?

12 A basketball arena has room for 20 000 people plus overflow space
for an extra $\frac{1}{10}$ of this number of people.

There are 12 gates to this arena.
For one match, the table below shows how many people went through each gate.

Gate 1 1273	Gate 2 1614	Gate 3 1389	Gate 4 1418
Gate 5 2172	Gate 6 1905	Gate 7 2712	Gate 8 1849
Gate 9 2178	Gate 10 1819	Gate 11 1567	Gate 12 1872

Was there enough room in the arena for this number of people?

Explain your answer.

N | NUMBER 2EXT

1   Jamie works out that

$$\frac{2}{5} + \frac{1}{3} = \frac{3}{8}$$

Explain clearly the mistake that Jamie has made.
Without using a calculator, work out the correct answer, showing all steps clearly.

2   Asha spends $\frac{1}{5}$ of her money on a mask and $\frac{1}{4}$ of her money on food.

What fraction of her money has she now got left?

3   In Clegg's factory, a machine takes $8\frac{1}{2}$ minutes to fill a box with chocolates and to wrap the box. The machine starts up at 06:00. Will the machine deal with 30 boxes by 10:00? Give reasons for your answer.

4

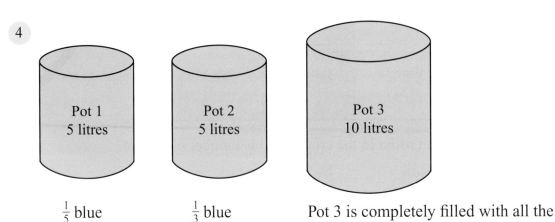

Pot 1
5 litres

Pot 2
5 litres

Pot 3
10 litres

$\frac{1}{5}$ blue

$\frac{4}{5}$ yellow

$\frac{1}{3}$ blue

$\frac{2}{3}$ yellow

Pot 3 is completely filled with all the paint shown from pots 1 and 2. What fraction of pot 3 is yellow paint?

5 (a) Rosa needs to work out $9 \div \frac{1}{4}$

She says that the answer is $9 \times 4 = 36$

This is the correct answer for $9 \div \frac{1}{4}$

Explain *why* Rosa's method gives the correct answer.

(b) Work out $9 \div \frac{3}{4}$

6 120 people in 'Burgers Я Us' are asked how often they buy a hamburger.

280 people in the 'Burger Banquet' are asked how often they buy a hamburger.

$\frac{2}{3}$ of these people in 'Burgers Я Us' say they buy a hamburger once a month.

$\frac{4}{7}$ of these people in 'Burger Banquet' say they buy a hamburger once a month.

What fraction of *all* the people above say they buy a hamburger once a month?

7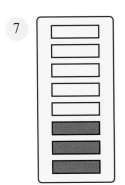

This shows the amount of fuel in Avery's car.

Each bar shows $\frac{1}{8}$ of the petrol in the car's tank.

A full petrol tank contains 40 litres.

A litre of petrol costs £1.68.

How much money will it cost Avery to fill the petrol tank up completely?

Hint:
Firstly work out how many litres of petrol are shown by one bar.

8   Find the fraction that is exactly half way between

$$\frac{3}{8} \text{ and } \frac{2}{5}$$

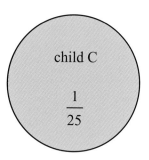

Hint:

Firstly write $\frac{3}{8}$ as $\frac{30}{80}$

9   Sophie's three children eat cereal every morning for their breakfast.

The fraction of a box of cereal eaten each morning by each child is shown below.

child A $\frac{1}{25}$

child B $\frac{2}{25}$

child C $\frac{1}{25}$

What is the least number of boxes of cereal that Sophie will need to buy to last the entire month of June?

Explain your working out fully.

10

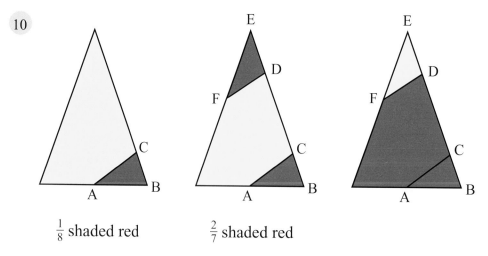

$\frac{1}{8}$ shaded red $\frac{2}{7}$ shaded red

What fraction of the triangle is shaded red in the last diagram?

11 Simplify $\dfrac{1}{m} + \dfrac{1}{n}$

This means you need to add the fractions together with your normal rules and the answer will be a single fraction with m and n in it.

12 Cooper's dog weighs 19.4 kg.
The amount of dog food from a can to be eaten each day is shown below.

Weight of dog (kg)	Amount of food
Up to 11	$\frac{1}{4}$ can
11 to 20	$\frac{1}{3}$ can
20 to 30	$\frac{1}{2}$ can

Cooper buys the dog food from his local store.
The prices are shown in the table below.

1 can for 60p

3 cans for £1.70

6 cans for £3.20

Cooper wants to buy enough cans of dog food for all the month of March. What is the least amount of money he must spend?
Explain your answer fully.

M | MIXED 2A

1 Jason needs to simplify an algebraic expression.
He decides that $5a + 2a + 3b - a + 2b$ is the same as $6a + 5b$.
Is he correct? If not, what mistake has he made?

2 Renata parks her car in a city
supermarket car park.

The first $1\frac{1}{2}$ hours is free of charge.

After that, Renata has to pay 60p for
every 20 minutes or part of 20 minutes.

How much does Renata pay if she arrives
at 1:15 p.m. and leaves the car park at 4:30 p.m.?

3 In this question, $a = -3$ and $b = -4$

Which two expressions below give the same
answer?

$a^2 + b$ $3(2a - b)$ $a - 2b$

Give full reasons for your answer.

Hint:
A negative number
multiplied by a negative
number gives a positive
number.
Subtracting a negative
number is the same as
adding the number.

4 $1\,\text{kg} = 1000$ grams so $250\,\text{g} = \frac{1}{4}\,\text{kg}$.
Rachel is making cakes.
She has $12\,\text{kg}$ of flour and $10\,\text{kg}$ of butter.
She needs $\frac{1}{4}\,\text{kg}$ of flour for each cake and $\frac{1}{5}\,\text{kg}$ of butter for each cake.
Work out the greatest number of cakes that Rachel could make.

5   The Taylor family are in the USA.
The whole family want to spend 2 hours
swimming with dolphins at the
Marine Centre in Florida.
The prices are shown below.

THE MARINE CENTRE	
One hour swim with dolphins	
Adult	$54
Child	$39
Family ticket	$160
(2 adults and 2 children)	

The Taylor family consist of 2 adults and
4 children.

What is the least amount of money they
could spend for their swim?

6   The number 36 is the highest common factor of
two numbers which lie between 100 and 200.
Write down what these two numbers might be.

Hint:
Examine multiples
of 36.

7   Which of these fractions is the larger?

$$\frac{4}{5} \text{ or } \frac{5}{7}$$

You must fully explain your answer.

8   The number 4 is the common factor of $4n + 12$ so $4n + 12$ factorises to $4(n + 3)$.
Tom multiplies out the brackets below so that $3(5n + 4) + 2(3n + 3) = 3(an + b)$
Work out the values of a and b.

9 Simon works on a building site. He is paid £8.80 per hour for an 8 hour day. He is paid time and half for working any hours above 8 hours.

On Monday he worked on four houses for the times shown below.

House A: 2 hours 20 minutes

House B: 3 hours 45 minutes

House C: 50 minutes

House D: 2 hours 35 minutes

How much money does Simon earn on Monday?

10 Find three different prime numbers which add together to give a total of 47.

11 Ashna uses rules of indices to write the following:

$$\frac{(2^4)^2 \times 2^3}{2^5}$$

$$= \frac{2^6 \times 2^3}{2^5}$$

$$= \frac{2^9}{2^5}$$

$$= 2^4$$

Maya says that Ashna has made a mistake.

(a) Explain what mistake she has made.

(b) Work out what the final simplified answer should be.

12 The cost price and selling price of peppers in a local store are shown below.

Colour	Cost price	Selling price
Green	55p	80p
Yellow	40p	70p
Red	45p	75p

On Thursday the store manager buys 50 of each colour of pepper.

The store manager uses some of these to make 12 multipacks containing one pepper of each colour.

The selling price of each multipack is £1.90

The remaining peppers are sold individually.

At the end of the day the peppers shown below have not been sold.

Green	Yellow	Red	Multipack
2	5	3	4

Work out how much profit the store makes on the sale of peppers on that Thursday.
Show all your working out clearly.

M   MIXED 2EXT

1 $2\frac{1}{5} \times 3\frac{2}{3} = 6\frac{2}{15}$ Is this answer true or false?

Give full reasons for your answer.

2

B

$x + 2$

A   C

$3x + 4$

D

In the kite opposite, AB = BC and AD = CD.
The perimeter of the square below is equal to the
perimeter of the kite.

Work out the value of x if one side of the square
is 11 cm.

3   The number 25 has only 3 factors: 1, 5 and 25.

(a) Find at least 3 other numbers which have exactly 3 factors only.

(b) Write down any ideas you used to speed up your search.

4

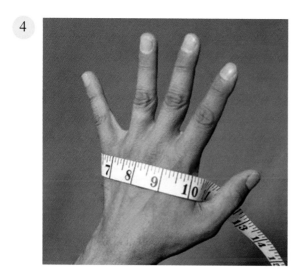

Paige has a piece of ribbon. She
uses $\frac{2}{5}$ of the ribbon on a present
for her mother and another $\frac{1}{3}$ of the
ribbon on a gift for her sister.

She has 52 cm of ribbon left over.

How long was the piece of ribbon to
begin with?

Hint:

If $\frac{2}{9}$ of a length is 16 cm

then $\frac{1}{9}$ is 16 ÷ 2 = 8 cm

so $\frac{9}{9}$ is 8 × 9 = 72 cm

5 A jar contains (1.5×10^3) pencil clips.
Some similar jars are placed in a box.
The box now contains (1.5×10^4) pencil clips.

(a) How many jars are in the box?

(b) Explain clearly how you worked out your answer to part (a).

(c) How many jars would be in the box if it now contained (1.5×10^5) pencil clips?

6 Robert sells caravans for 'Harrison's caravans'. He is paid £890 each month plus a bonus if he sells more than 8 caravans as shown below.

> Bonus payment: £125 for each extra caravan sold above 8.

Melanie sells caravans for 'Vanpark'.
She is paid £10 320 per year.
She also gets a monthly bonus if she sells more than 9 caravans as shown opposite.

> Bonus:
>
> £100 for 1 extra sale above 9
> £300 for 2 extra sales above 9
> £550 for 3 extra sales above 9
> £850 for 4 extra sales above 9

(a) In April they both sell 12 caravans. Who earns more money that month and by how much?

(b) In May they both sell 11 caravans. Does the same person still earn more money?
Explain your answer fully.

7   $4^m \times 4^n = 4^6$

If $m = n$, work out the value of 4^{-m}.

Hint:
Remember that
$$a^{-n} = \frac{1}{a^n}$$

8   Two numbers A and B are broken down into prime factors which are shown in the Venn diagram below.

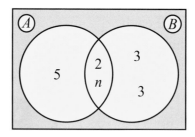

If the lowest common multiple (LCM) of A and B is 630, work out the values of A and B.

9

house   brother   Adrian   pub

Adrian and his brother want to walk $7\frac{1}{2}$ miles from their house to a pub.
The brother leaves their house one hour after Adrian.

The brother has travelled $4\frac{1}{3}$ miles when Adrian is $1\frac{3}{5}$ miles from the pub.

How far is the brother behind Adrian at this instant?

10 Molly has £1400 for a fortnight's holiday in Egypt. She looks on the internet and finds the information below.

Flights		
From Manchester to Cairo (Egypt)	From Cairo to Manchester	
6:20 am £270	10:15 pm £235	
9:45 am £440	1:05 pm £79	

Hotels: rate per night	
2*	£55
3*	£75
4*	£95
5*	£125

Molly needs to fly from Manchester but will not fly at night. She does not want to stay in a basic 2* hotel.

Molly must stay within her budget.

Which flights and hotels can she choose?

You must write down all your calculations clearly to show that Molly is within her budget.

11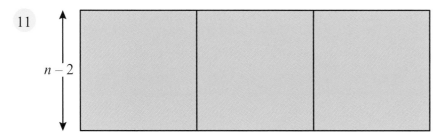

$n - 2$

A rectangle is made from 3 squares as shown above.

Teresa works out an expression for the area of this rectangle and simplifies it to:

$$3n^2 - 12n + 12$$

Is Teresa correct? If not, work out the correct answer.

12   A farmer has some fields which make a large square.

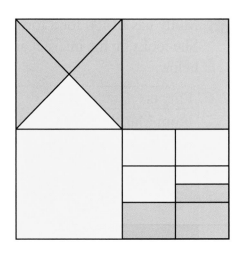

If the large square was all planted with wheat, the farmer would make £25 440 profit.

If the large square had nothing planted in it, the government would pay the farmer £4152.

The farmer plants some wheat (green area) and leaves some land with nothing planted on it (yellow area).

Work out how much the farmer will make in total.

G | GEOMETRY 1A

1 Calculate the value of angle x.

Show your working out clearly.

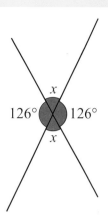

2 Draw any quadrilateral which has 2 lines of symmetry only and order of rotational symmetry 2.

3

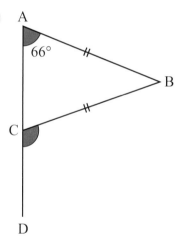

Find the value of angle BCD.
You must give all your reasons.

Find the value of angle QRS.
You must give all your reasons.

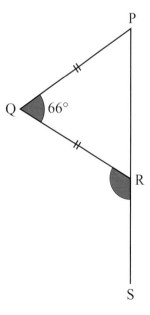

4 The letter $\mathbb{M}$ is drawn on a graph.

(a) This letter is reflected in the *x*-axis. What letter will it now look like?

(b) What will this letter look like now if it is reflected in the *y*-axis to start with and not the *x*-axis?

5

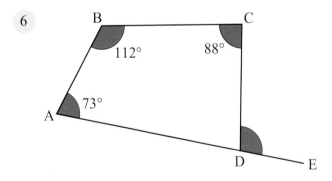

A square is attached to a regular hexagon as shown.

Work out the value of angle *x*.

Explain your working out fully.

Hint:
Maybe split the hexagon into 4 triangles to find out what all the interior angles of the hexagon add up to.

6

Find the value of angle CDE.
You must give all your reasons.

7

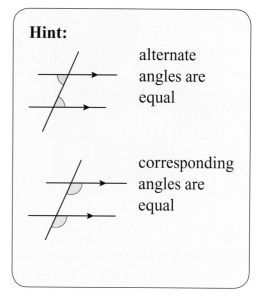

ACDF is a rectangle.

Lines BF and CE are parallel.

Work out the value of angle BCE.

You must give reasons to explain your answer.

8 Kelly (K) is standing at co-ordinates (6, 1).

Alan is standing at co-ordinates (1, 5).
Riya is standing half way between Kelly and Alan.

Write down the co-ordinates of the point where Riya is standing.

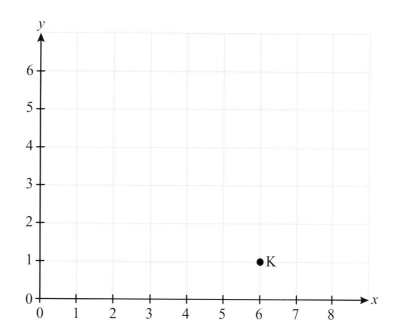

9 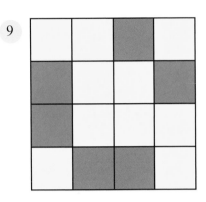 Copy and shade two more squares so that this pattern has rotational symmetry of order 4.

10 Calculate the size of angle ABE.
You must give reasons to explain
your answer.

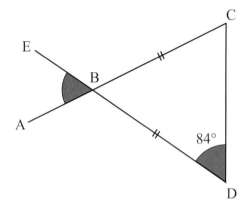

11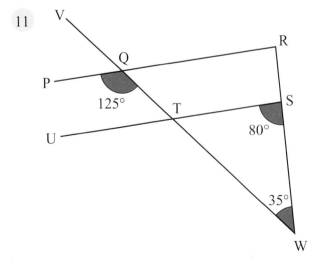

(a) Work out the value of SṪW.

(b) Explain clearly whether straight line PQR is parallel to straight line STU or not?

12

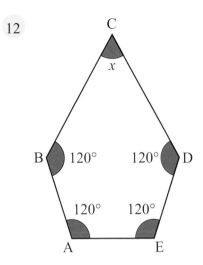

ABCDE is a pentagon.

Calculate the size of the angle marked x.

Give reasons for your answer.

G | GEOMETRY 1B

1 A shape P is translated with vector $\begin{pmatrix} 5 \\ -3 \end{pmatrix}$.

Its image is then translated back to the original position of shape P with vector $\begin{pmatrix} a \\ b \end{pmatrix}$.

Write down the values of a and b.

2 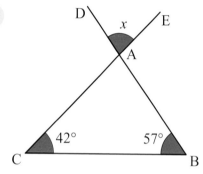 Work out the size of the angle marked x. You must give reasons for each step in your working.

3 The equilateral triangle BDF is shown inside the rectangle ACEG.

Calculate $E\widehat{D}F$.

Show all your working out.

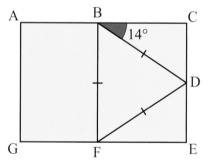

4 Draw a trapezium which has no line of symmetry.

5

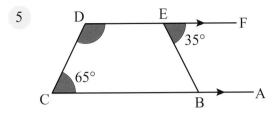

Lines DF and CA are parallel.
Work out the value of angle CDE.
You must give full reasons for your answer.

6

Calculate the angle x at the top of Joe's kite.
Explain your working fully.

Hint:
The angles in a quadrilateral add up to 360°.

7 Work out the size of the angle marked x.
Give reasons for your answer.

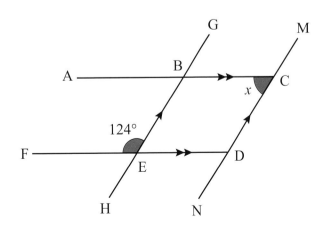

8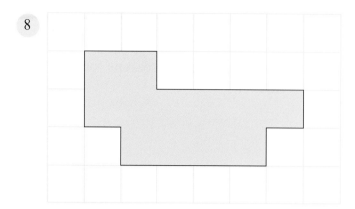

The shape opposite is enlarged by scale factor 3.

Each square is 1 cm².

Work out the perimeter of the enlarged shape, *without drawing it*.

9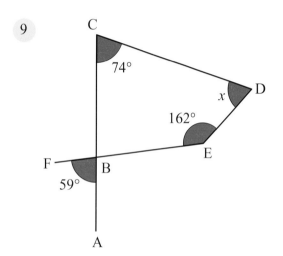

Calculate the size of the angle marked *x*. You must give reasons to explain your answer.

10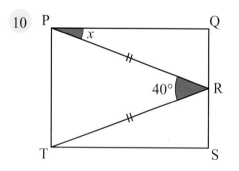

PQST is a rectangle.

PRT is an isosceles triangle.
Work out the size of the angle marked *x*.
Give reasons for your answer.

11

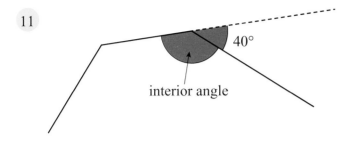

40°

interior angle

The diagram opposite shows part of a regular polygon and one of its exterior angles.

Work out the sum of all the interior angles of this regular polygon.

Hint:
All the exterior angles of a regular polygon add up to 360°.

12

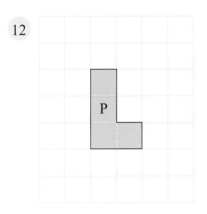

P

Draw a design which uses the shape P shown opposite and two further shapes. One of these shapes must be an enlargement of shape P with scale factor 2. The other shape must be an enlargement of shape P with scale factor 3.

G | GEOMETRY 1 EXT

1

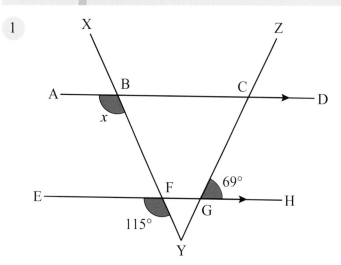

Work out the size of the angle marked x.
Give reasons for your answer.

2 A point P is translated to a point Q with vector $\begin{pmatrix} 4 \\ 3 \end{pmatrix}$.

The point Q is translated to a point R with vector $\begin{pmatrix} -6 \\ 2 \end{pmatrix}$.

Write down the vector which would translate point R to point P.

3

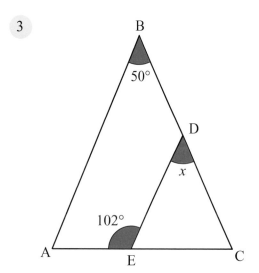

Triangle ABC is isosceles with AB = BC.

Work out the value of angle x.

Give full reasons in your working out.

4

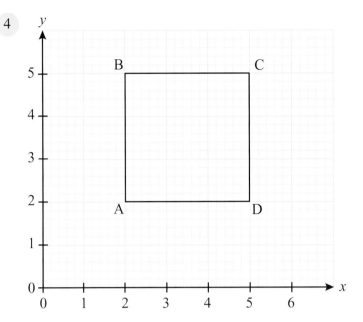

Square ABCD is reflected in the line $y = x$ followed by a 90° clockwise rotation about the point A.

(a) Write down the co-ordinates of D.

(b) Copy the diagram and draw the new shapes if needed. Write down the co-ordinates of D after the reflection and rotation.

(c) What do you notice about your answers to parts (a) and (b)?

5 One angle in an isosceles triangle is 40°. Write down the values of the other angles in the isosceles triangle. *You must make sure you give all the possible answers there might be.*

6

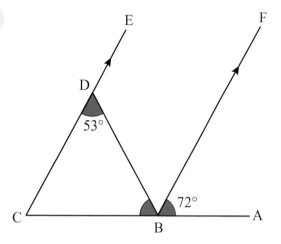

Calculate the size of angle CBD.

You must give reasons for each step in your working.

7 A shape in a computer game needs to be moved on the screen.

The following instructions are used:

(a) Rotate the shape 90° anticlockwise about A.

(b) Translate the shape with $\begin{pmatrix} -5 \\ -1 \end{pmatrix}$

(c) Now translate the shape with $\begin{pmatrix} 0 \\ -4 \end{pmatrix}$

Draw the shape on squared paper. Show the new position of the shape.

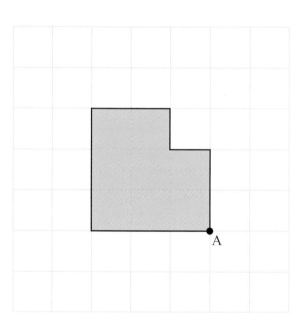

8

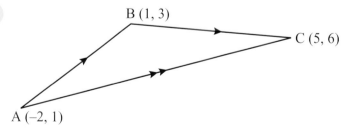

Explain clearly why $\overrightarrow{AB} + \overrightarrow{BC} = \overrightarrow{AC}$

Hint:
Use column vectors. e.g.

Q (3, 9)

P (1, 4) $\overrightarrow{PQ} = \begin{pmatrix} 2 \\ 5 \end{pmatrix}$

9

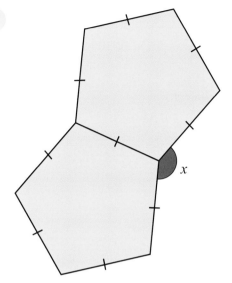

The diagram shows two regular pentagons joined together. Calculate the value of angle x.

Explain your reasons fully.

10 (a) Draw x and y axes both labelled from -6 to 6.

  (b) Draw a triangle with vertices at $(-4, 5)$, $(-4, 4)$ and $(-2, 4)$.

  (c) This triangle is reflected in the line $y = -x$ then the new triangle is reflected in the line $y = 4$. Write down the co-ordinates of the point (or points) which remain *invariant* following these two transformations.

> **Hint:**
> An invariant point means its position is left unchanged by the transformation.

11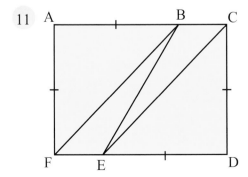

ACDF is a rectangle.

Triangle ABF is isosceles.

Triangle CDE is isosceles.

Prove that triangles BEF and BCE are congruent.

12

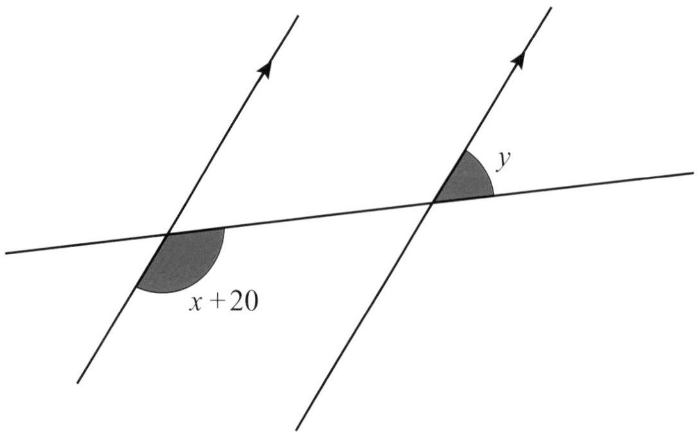

$x + 20$

y

Express angle y in terms of x.

N | NUMBER 3A

1 Anya spends $\frac{7}{12}$ of her time on a computer playing games. Write down the ratio for the time spent playing games compared to the time spent not playing games.

2 Evan is replacing some fencing. He buys the following items.
The cost of each item is also given.

4 fence panels	£12.99 each
5 posts	£7.50 each
2 packets of screws	£3.85 each

Evan pays with five £20 notes. How much change will he get?

3

Type of food	Cost (week 1)	% change for week 2
Loaf of bread	£1.20	5% rise
Potatoes	64p per kg	stays same
Apples	85p per kg	20% drop
Pint of milk	50p	4% rise
Carrots	£1.40 per kg	5% drop
Bunch of 5 bananas	£1.10	stays same

In week 1 Vadim buys two loaves of bread,
5 kg of potatoes, 2 kg of apples, 3 pints of milk,
2 kg of carrots and 10 bananas.
He buys exactly the same amounts in week 2.
How much more or less does he spend in week 2?
Explain your working fully.

4

Electricity Bill

New reading   65248 units
Old reading   64897 units

Price per unit   36p

This is part of Ryan's electricity bill. Work out how much Ryan has to pay for his electricity.

Hint:
Subtract the old reading from the new reading to find out how many units of electricity have been used.

5

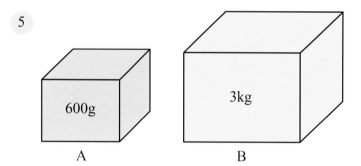

600g

A

3kg

B

Hint:
1 kg = 1000 g

Explain why weight of box A : weight of box B = 1 : 5

6 Copy and complete the bill shown below:

AUTO TYRES			
Item	Number	Price per item	Cost
Tyre	4	£41.20	
Air filter	1	£15.80	
Brake pad	2	£16.50	
Labour: 2 hours at £41.20 per hour			
VAT (Value Added Tax) at 20%			
Total cost			

7 The exchange rates in London and Berlin one day are shown opposite.

| London £1 = €1.16 |
| Berlin €1 = 87p |

Evelyn is travelling from London to Berlin. She has £800 to change into euros (€). Will she get more euros in London or Berlin? How many more euros will she get?

8 Julia has £700 to buy a new computer which is priced at £700.

The computer price is reduced by 20% in a sale.

This new computer price is then lowered by 15% of the new price.

If Julia now buys the computer, will she have enough money left to buy a £250 laptop as well?

You must give full reasons for your answer.

9 Anya has £35 to spend on petrol and a car wash.

Her car travels 9 miles for every one litre of petrol.

Petrol price   £1.49 per litre

Anya must put enough petrol into her car to travel 180 miles. What is the most expensive car wash setting she can afford from the list below after she has paid for her petrol? You must show all your working out.

CAR WASH	
Wash	£4.20
Wash including 4 wheel scrub	£4.80
Wash and dry, including 4 wheel scrub	£5.50
Full wash and wax shine	£6.50

10 (a) Copy and complete the lower box for this phone bill.

Account number: SS 5372 1941

PHONE BILL TOTAL NOW DUE			
Cost of calls			
UK landline	Daytime	73 calls	£38.16
	Evening/weekend	136 calls	£29.14
To a mobile	Daytime	53 calls	£53.94
	Evening/weekend	69 calls	£38.26

Cost of calls	?
Line rental	£15.70
Total	?
VAT @ 20%	?
Due total	?

(b) The phone bill is paid in three equal monthly instalments.
Calculate the cost of one monthly instalment.

11 The price of a coat is reduced by 10% in a sale and now costs £180.
The price of a shirt is reduced by 25% in the same sale and now costs £15.
How much more did the coat cost compared to the shirt *before* the sale?
Show all your working out clearly.

12 Logan, Anjali, Naomi and Gavin want to see a film
at the cinema. A ticket at the Cresswall Cinema is £7.60.
A ticket at the Albert Cinema is £6.50.

The friends can get to the Cresswall Cinema by bus
for £7.90 return. There is no bus to the Albert Cinema.

They can get a taxi to either cinema.

Cost of taxi   £1.30 per mile.

Which cinema and type of transport will be the cheapest
option for the 4 friends if the Cresswall Cinema is 12 miles
away and the Albert Cinema is 14 miles away? Explain your reasons.

N | NUMBER 3B

1 Chad says that $\frac{4}{5}$ is the same as 45%.

Is he correct? If not, explain clearly why he has made a mistake.

2 Copy and complete this bill.

NORTON'S CHINA SHOP			
Number of items	Item	Cost of one item	Total
4	Cup	£8.50	£_ _ _ _
5	Plate	£14.65	£73.25
3	Dish	£15.85	£_ _ _ _
2	Bowl	£_ _ _ _	£54.40
		Total	£_ _ _ _
		VAT at 20%	£_ _ _ _
		Total bill	£_ _ _ _

3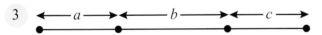

$a:b = 5:4$ and $b:c = 12:13$

Work out the ratio $a:c$

Give the answer in its simplest form.

> **Hint:**
> Convert the ratios so that the b values in each ratio are the same.

4 Marcus wants to buy an i-pod. He tries three different stores.

Techshow	Marleys	E-market
£260	£210	£250
$\frac{1}{5}$ off		15% reduction

Which store offers the lowest price for Marcus?
Show your working out.

5   Mr. Kennion, his wife and their three children like
    to swim often each week. They want to buy monthly
    swimming passes for their local pool.
    The prices are shown below:

Monthly pass prices	
Adult	£30
Child	£20
Senior Citizen	£22
Student	£22
Family	£72
(2 adults and 2 children)	

Mr. Kennion works at the pool and so he gets a 30% discount on all prices.

Work out the total he must pay for swimming passes for his entire family.

6   Anya earns £560 each week.
    She works very hard so on 8th March
    she is given a 4% pay rise.

    On the 7th May she is paid a bonus
    of £850.

    How much does Anya earn in total
    between 8th March and 23rd May?

7   Blake, Sophie and Raina are paid in the ratio $7:2:3$ respectively.
    Blake is paid £260 more than Raina.
    How much money is Sophie paid?
    Show all your working out.

8 Austin, Layla and Jason are on holiday in Spain. Austin has some money. He gives 20% of the money to Layla.

He gives $\frac{1}{2}$ of the money to Jason.

He now has 450 euros left over.

How many euros did Austin have before he gave some of the money away?

9 Carlos wants to build a wall. He needs to buy 480 bricks.
He finds three deals on the internet.

Deal 2
£17 for a box of 16 bricks
Buy 5 boxes and get one extra box free

Deal 1
£26 for a box of 32 bricks

Deal 3
£70 for a box of 80 bricks
10% discount on 5 or more boxes

Which deal will cost Carlos the least money?
Explain your reasons fully.

10   Alexia borrows £2400. She pays back 3% simple interest for 4 years then
     repays all the borrowed money.

     Chang borrows £1920 and pays back
     5% simple interest for 3 years.
     He then repays all the borrowed
     money.

     Who pays more money in interest
     by the time all the money has
     been repaid?
     Explain your answer fully.

> **Hint:**
> 'Simple interest' means
> the interest paid back each
> year remains the same.

11   Shreya completes a Science exam which is made up of 3 sections.

     Section A is worth 50 marks, section B is worth 30 marks and section C is
     worth 20 marks.

     Shreya scores 32 marks on section A, $\frac{5}{6}$ of the marks for section B and 55% of
     the marks for section C.

     What is Shreya's final total mark for this Science exam?

12   The boss of a small firm wants to give each person in the firm a hand painted
     Easter egg.

> **Plan A**
> £9 for every
> 5 eggs

> **Plan B**
> £2 for each egg. 1 free egg
> for every 20 eggs bought.

     The boss needs to buy an egg for each of 90 people.

     Which is cheaper – plan A or plan B? Give reasons for your answer.

N NUMBER 3C

1

CENTRAL GAS COMPANY
Previous reading 21784
Present reading 26159
@ 13.8p per unit of gas
Fixed quarterly charge £48.75

Hansen's furniture store receives its quarterly gas bill as shown opposite. Its monthly electricity bill is £107.62. Hansen's furniture store cannot allow its combined gas/electricity bills to exceed £1000 for this quarter (3 months). How much above or below £1000 are its combined gas/electricity bills?

2 Mary rounds the number 0.030764 to three significant figures and gives the answer as 0.0308
Jack says the answer should be 0.031
Explain clearly who is correct and why?

3 Alex wants to buy a camera. He tries the 3 shops below.

ELECTRO	SHUTTER	MATSONS
Camera	Camera	Camera
£261	£150	Deposit £30
$\frac{1}{3}$ off shown price	plus VAT at 20%	plus 12 monthly payments of £11.50

Which shop offers Alex the cheapest deal?
Explain your reasons fully.

4   Five different ratios are shown below.
    Four of them are equivalent to the ratio 4 : 3
    Which is the odd one out?
    You must show all your working out.

> **Hint:**
> 1 km = 1000 m
> 1 kg = 1000 g

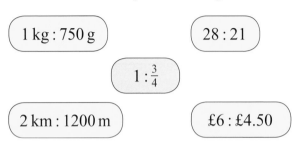

(1 kg : 750 g)   (28 : 21)

(1 : $\frac{3}{4}$)

(2 km : 1200 m)   (£6 : £4.50)

5

225 g pack of butter	£1.68
Tin of baked beans	57p
2.5 kg bag of potatoes	£1.74
Pint of milk	52p
6 pots of yoghurt	£1.65

Jenny has £3.50 in her pocket. Her mother gives her a £10 note.
She goes to the supermarket and buys items at the prices shown above.

Does she have enough money to buy two 225 g packs of butter, 3 pints of milk,
12 pots of yoghurt, 5 kg of potatoes and 3 tins of baked beans?

If she has enough money, how much will she have left over after paying for all
the shopping?

If she did not have enough money, how much money did she need?

6

> Chocolates
>
> 4.14 euros
>
> 250 g

Maurice is in Bruges and buys the Belgium chocolates shown opposite.

When he gets back to England, he finds $\frac{1}{2}$ kg of the same type of chocolates being sold for £7.76

> Exchange rate
>
> £1 = 1.15 euros

In which country were the chocolates better value for money, Belgium or England? Show all your working out.

7 A 500 ml drink called 'orange explosion' contains 300 ml of water. Would 750 ml of the same drink contain more or less than 450 ml of water? Explain your answer.

8 A teacher wants to explain why $0.3 \times 0.24 = 0.072$

(a) Firstly the teacher changes 0.3 and 0.24 into fractions.

(b) Next the teacher multiplies these two fractions together.

(c) Finally the teacher changes the fraction answer back into a decimal.

> **Hint:**
> To multiply together two fractions, multiply the numerators together then multiply the denominators together.

Show clearly everything the teacher did above. Does it give the correct answer to the decimal multiplication?

9 At the start of the year in one part of the Atlantic Ocean there are 3000 sealions and 3000 dolphins. By the end of the year, the population of sealions drops by 8% and the number of dolphins rises by 3%.

What is the difference in the number of sealions and the number of dolphins by the end of the year?

10 Ken uses his van to transport furniture. He moves some furniture for Mrs. Thomas and gives her the bill shown below.

Kenny Move

Mrs. Thomas   Job number 312
5, Wayside
Leeds
LS10 5BM

10th March

number of units	Price per unit	Total	VAT (20%)
2 tables	£15	£30	£6
4 chairs	£6	£24	£5.20
1 bed	£20	£20	£4
1 wardrobe	£18	£18	£3.60
Total		£92 +	£18.80
		To pay	£110.80

Mrs Thomas spots a mistake on the bill.
What mistake has been made and what should be the total to pay?

11 Faith is in Japan and buys her mother a gift costing 11349 yen.

Her brother, Mark, is in the USA and buys his mother two gifts, one costing $39 and the other costing $49.92.
In pounds, who spent more money on gifts for their mother and by how much?

Exchange rates
£1 = $1.56
£1 = 194 yen

12 A skirt in a shop costs £40 before VAT is added on. A sale reduction of 15% is
    to be used. The shop can do plan A or plan B below:

Plan A	Plan B
Add the 20% VAT first then reduce the price by 15%.	Reduce the price by 15% first then add the 20% VAT.

Work out the final price using Plan A then Plan B.
Which plan gives the lower final price of the skirt and by how much?

N | NUMBER 3EXT

1 Hamish wants to invest £5000 for two years. Three banks offer the following deals.

EASY BANK	TRICKIER BANK	MAYBE BANK
Fixed rate 4% per annum Compound interest	1st year : 3% per annum 2nd year : 5% per annum	Fixed rate 3% per annum compound interest plus bonus of £100 at the end of 2 years

Which bank should Hamish use to make the most money? Show your full working out.

> **Hint:**
> Remember that 'compound interest' means that the interest changes each year and is based on how much money is in the account at that moment.

2 24 tubes of red and blue paint are mixed in the ratio 3 : 5.

18 tubes of blue and yellow paint are mixed in the ratio 2 : 7.

How many tubes of blue paint were used in total?

3 Teresa needs to divide 14 by 0.2 but has no calculator.
She multiplies both numbers by 10 then works out $140 \div 2$
which gives the answer 70.

(a) Does this mean that $14 \div 0.2 = 70$?

(b) Explain exactly how you know that the answer
in part (a) is correct or not correct?

Hint:

$$0.2 = \frac{2}{10} = \frac{1}{5}$$

4 In 2011 the ratio of old factories to modern
factories is $2 : 3$ in parts of the UK.
There are actually 17250 modern factories.

In 2012, half the old factories are knocked
down and rebuilt as modern factories.

What is the new ratio of old factories to
modern factories?

5 Tom is a student. He lives on a total of £7500 for the year.
45% of the money comes from a student loan.
His parents give him 30% of the money.

He earns the rest of the money by delivering papers and
doing bar work in the ratio $9 : 16$.

How much money does he earn from the bar work?

6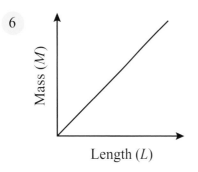

Mass (M)

Length (L)

The graph opposite shows that the mass M of an object is directly proportional to its length L.

(a) It is known that $M = 20$ when $L = 5$.
    Explain why $M = 4L$

(b) Work out the value of M when $L = 17$.

(c) If the value of L is halved, what happens to the value of M?

7 Kitty says 'if you increase a number by 50% then increase this answer by 50%, the result will be the same as doubling the original number'.
Explain clearly whether Kitty is correct or not.

8 Jocelyn receives some money from her uncle.
She spends $\frac{1}{5}$ of the money on clothes.
She spends 40% of the money on a computer.
She spends $\frac{3}{8}$ of the money on a holiday.
If she spent £192 on the clothes, how much money did she have left after all the spending?

9 Mr Kenwood is working out the cost of his next gas bill.

Gas Meter Readings

Previous reading: 31789
Present reading: 33004

He has to pay:

16.8p for the first 400 units used

11.2p for the remaining units used

How much will Mr Kenwood have to pay for this gas bill?

10　The price of a jacket is reduced by 20% in a sale. The jacket now costs £48.

Kayla wants to find out the original price of the jacket so she does the following calculation:

20% of 48 = 0.2 × 48 = 9.60
original cost = 48 + 9.60 = £57.60

(a) Explain clearly what mistake Kayla has made.

(b) Work out the original cost of the jacket.

11　Three people take 4 hours to pack 2400 identical mugs into boxes.

(a) If four people each work at the same rate as the three people, how many identical mugs will the four people pack into boxes in 4 hours?

(b) Assuming they work at the same rate, how much time will be saved by eight people packing the 2400 identical mugs into boxes compared to just three people doing the packing?

12　Austin wants to invest £2000 in a bank for 2 years.
He looks at the two deals below:

ZPN Bank
5% per annum compound interest

Reece Bank
6% per annum simple interest
The bank charges a fee of 10% of the interest made when all the money is withdrawn

Austin will take out all the money after 2 years.

Which deal is the best for Austin and by how much?

PART TWO

M MIXED 3A

1 A shop is closing down and so it has a clearance sale.

CLEARANCE SALE

$\frac{1}{3}$ off normal prices

plus an extra 20% off sale prices

Danielle buys a pair of shoes (normal price £108)
and a skirt (normal price £75).

How much will she pay in total in the sale?

2 Chris says that 'when numbers with indices are multiplied together,
add the powers.'

He works out the two questions below:

(a) $3^2 \times 3^2 = 9^4$ (b) $3^2 \times 2^3 = 6^5$

Do you agree with his answers? If not, explain his mistakes and work out the
correct answers.

3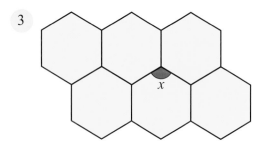

Regular hexagons tessellate
(fit together with no gaps).

Explain clearly why there are no gaps.

Hint:
Work out the value of angle x first.

4 165 has prime factors 3, 5 and m.
170 has prime factors 2, 5 and n.
Work out the values of m and n.
Write down the difference between m and n.

5 Aidan needs to bake enough
bakewell tarts for 53 people.
The recipe for the pastry
is shown below.

Pastry (for 8 people)	
125 g	plain flour
75 g	butter
25 g	sugar
1	egg

The plain flour is sold in 500 g bags. How many bags must Aidan buy to make all the bakewell tarts? Explain your working out fully.

6 Aaron needs to buy a new washing machine.
He finds the machine he wants in three different stores.
The prices are shown below:

DAWSONS	WASHWELL	LECTROSTORE
£420	£499.99	£500
+VAT	(including VAT)	15% discount then +VAT

Which store offers the cheapest deal for Aaron if VAT = 20%?
You must show all your working out.

7 Tabi says that the expression $6(3n - 5)$ is identical to the expression $2(9n - 15)$.
Is she correct or not? Give a reason for your answer.

8 There are 240 students in the Sixth Form at Horton Hill High School.
60% of these students go to the nearby Glastonbury festival.
$\frac{2}{3}$ of these people who go to the festival share a tent.
$\frac{1}{2}$ of these tent people are male.

What fraction of all the Sixth Form students are females who share a tent at the festival?

9 Hannah buys a sketchpad for £12.50 to take on her holiday to Italy.
She fills up the pad in Rome so has to buy another sketchpad.
She pays 13.8 euros for her new sketchpad.

Is this cheaper or more expensive than her first sketchpad and by how much? The exchange rate is shown below.

£1 = 1.15 euros

10 Some orange squash is mixed with water.
Three different drinks are made.
The proportion of each drink which is squash is shown below:

① squash = $\frac{1}{10}$

② squash = 9.5%

③ squash : water = 2 : 19

Hint:
The ratio $a : b = \dfrac{a}{b}$

$a \div b$ converts $\dfrac{a}{b}$ to a decimal.

Write down the drinks in order of size for the proportion of squash, starting with the largest. Give clear reasons for your answer.

11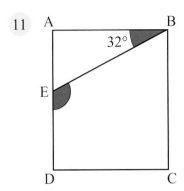

ABCD is a rectangle.

Work out the size of angle BED.

Give reasons for your answer.

12

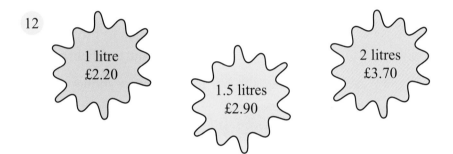

The prices of freshly squeezed orange juice are shown above.
Lian needs to buy 5 litres of this orange juice.
Which cartons should she buy so that she spends the least amount of money?

M | MIXED 3EXT

1 Kaitlyn needs to make the same cake in each of the four weeks in February. The cake recipe for 12 people includes:

210 g	plain chocolate
270 g	icing sugar
240 g	butter
6	egg whites
465 ml	thick cream
180 g	flour

Each week she needs to make the cake for 8 people. She decides to buy the icing sugar, flour and plain chocolate for all the cakes at the start of February.

Each of these ingredients is sold in two sizes in her local store as shown below.

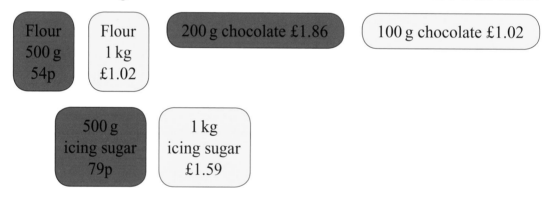

Flour 500 g 54p

Flour 1 kg £1.02

200 g chocolate £1.86

100 g chocolate £1.02

500 g icing sugar 79p

1 kg icing sugar £1.59

Calculate the least amount she must spend on the icing sugar, flour and plain chocolate.

2 Declan solves the equation as shown below:

$$4(2n + 5) = 32$$
$$8n + 20 = 32$$
$$8n = 32 - 20$$
$$8n = 12$$
$$n = \frac{12}{8} = \frac{3}{2} = 1\frac{1}{2}$$

Jess says he has made a mistake.
Who is correct? Give reasons for your answer.

3 Convert the ratio $\frac{3}{8} : \frac{5}{24} : \frac{1}{3}$ into the form $a : b : c$ where a, b and c are integers (whole numbers).

4 Sophie goes to India for three weeks. She changes £750 into rupees. The exchange rate is shown below.

$$£1 = 75 \text{ rupees}$$

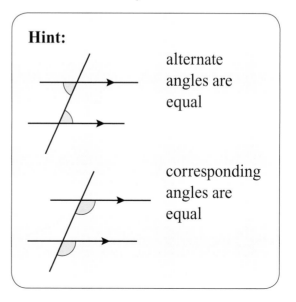

During her stay in India she spends 50340 rupees.

When Sophie returns home, she gives all the remaining money to her sister. Her sister needs £75 to see a music concert. Is Sophie's remaining money enough for this? Explain your answer fully.

5

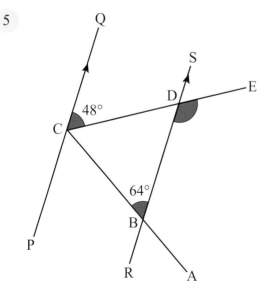

Lines PQ and RS are parallel.

Calculate the size of angle BDE.

Give reasons for your answer.

Hint:

alternate angles are equal

corresponding angles are equal

6

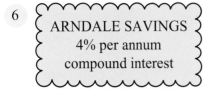

ARNDALE SAVINGS
4% per annum
compound interest

Ian invests £9000
in Arndale Savings.

Eva invests £6500
in Moxon Bank.

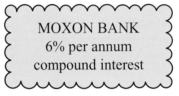

MOXON BANK
6% per annum
compound interest

Who gets the greater amount of interest after two years and by how much?

7   If a person does not pay the year's tax bill by
31st January, a penalty payment at £100
must be made.

For every month after 31st January that the tax
bill is not paid, the person will have to pay an
extra 2% of the tax bill.

Deven has a tax bill of £3800. How much must
he pay in total if he pays the bill on 10th March?

8

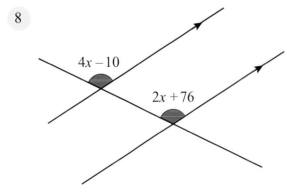

$4x - 10$

$2x + 76$

Find the value of x, hence
write down the actual values
of the two angles shown.

9 Grapefruit juice, blackcurrant juice and lemonade is mixed in the ratio 3 : 1 : 4 to make a juice cocktail.

(a) How much blackcurrant juice and lemonade is needed to make 16 litres of cocktail?

(b) Hunter needs 60 litres of drink for a party. He decides that one third of this will be juice cocktail. How much grapefruit juice will he need?

(c) What fraction of the cocktail is lemonade?

10 Gideon and Lauren are wanting to borrow £300 000 to buy a house. Gideon earns £24 000 and Lauren earns £41 000 each year.

The East Hilshire Building Society will lend them $4\frac{1}{2}$ times their joint salary.

The Paulton bank will lend them $5\frac{1}{2}$ times the larger salary and $3\frac{1}{2}$ times the smaller salary.

Who should Gideon and Lauren borrow from? Give full reasons for your answer.

11

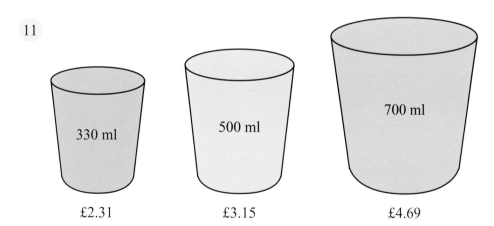

The prices of three different sized cups of cola at a cinema are shown above.

Which cup gives the *best value* for money? Explain your reasons fully.

12

BOOTS
15% OFF
Now £66.30

BAG
35% OFF
Now £34.45

Sofia finds some boots and a bag in the sales but cannot afford them until she gets paid the next day.

She goes back to the shop on the next day but finds the deals have changed. Both the boots and the bag now have 25% off in the sales. How much must Sofia now pay in total for the boots and the bag?

Hint:
Consider the 'reverse percentage' procedure first.

A | ALGEBRA 2A

1 Sequence A is 1, 3, 6, 10, …

Sequence B is 2, 3, 5, 8, …

The number 3 is in both sequences. What is the next highest number which is in both sequences?

Hint:
A Fibonacci sequence is when 'adding the two previous terms gives the next term'.

2 Copy the axes below.

Draw the graph of $y = 2x + 5$ for values of x from $x = -4$ to $x = 3$.

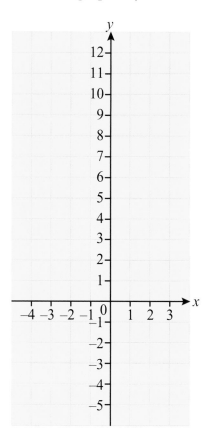

Hint:
Use the equation to make a table of values:

x							
y							

3   Each equation below is rearranged to make x the subject.
Write down which answers are correct. For each answer which is not correct,
explain clearly what mistake has been made.

Ⓐ $y = 5x$

$$\frac{y}{5} = x$$

Ⓑ $y = 5x + 3$

$$y + 3 = 5x$$

$$\frac{y + 3}{5} = x$$

Ⓒ $y = 5x - 7$

$$y + 7 = 5x$$

$$\frac{y + 7}{5} = x$$

4   Holly has 3 dogs, weighing
28 pounds, 20 pounds and 34 pounds.

She has to buy 'worming' packets
for each dog.
They are sold in the sizes shown
below.

Use the graph opposite to work out
which packets Holly must buy and
what the total cost will be.

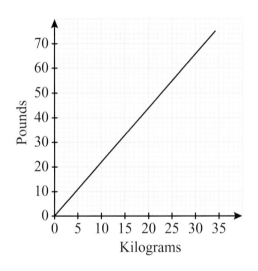

Pounds vs Kilograms

Worming
treatment
for dogs
of size
5 kg – 10 kg

£32

Worming
treatment
for dogs
of size
10 kg – 20 kg

£39

Worming
treatment
for dogs
of size
over 20 kg

£45

5   Arjun is making a matchstick sequence as shown:

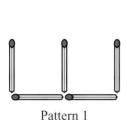  

Pattern 1   Pattern 2   Pattern 3

Arjun has 130 matchsticks in total.
How many matchstick patterns can he make and how many matchsticks will he
have left over?

6   Which two lines below are parallel to each other?
Give clear reasons for your answer.

Ⓐ $y = 6 - 5x$ Ⓑ $y = 5x + 4$ Ⓒ $y = -6x + 5$ Ⓓ $y = 6 + 5x$

7   Copy the axes shown.

Draw the graph of $y = x^2 + 2$ for
values of x from $x = -4$ to $x = 4$.

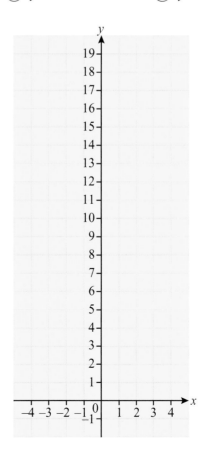

8   Andy and Kate each travel 80 miles from Andy's house to a shopping centre.
    On the way Andy stops for 45 minutes at a Service Station. Kate does not stop
    until she reaches the shopping centre. The graph below shows each person's
    journey.

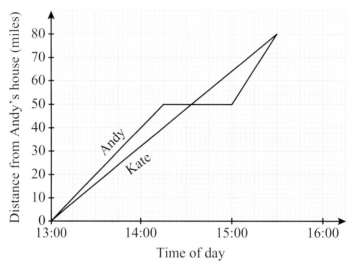

(a) At roughly what time does Kate pass the Service Station?

(b) At what speed does Andy travel from the Service Station to the shopping
    centre?

9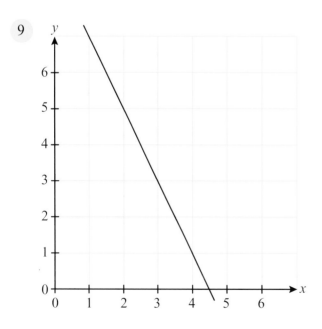

Explain clearly why the
gradient of the line shown
opposite cannot equal 2.

10 Jordan says that the formula $m = \dfrac{n}{5} - 8$ is exactly the same as the formula $n = 5m + 40$. Prove whether Jordan is correct or not.

11 Kate walked from her home to her grandparents' home, a total distance of 14 km. On her way she stopped for 30 minutes at a shop.

The first part of her journey is shown in the travel graph opposite.

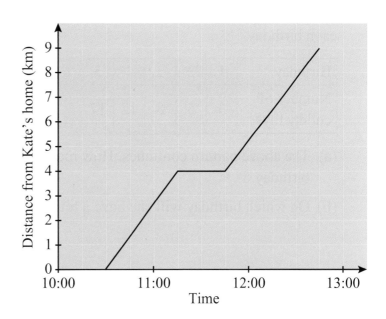

From 11:45 onwards she walked at a steady speed until she reached her grandparents' home. Some of this journey is shown in the travel graph.

(a) At what time did Kate reach her grandparents' home?

(b) Kate's brother cycled from their home to their grandparents' home at a steady speed of 7 km/h.
He wanted to reach their grandparents' home at exactly the same time as Kate. At what time did Kate's brother have to start his journey?

12 Throughout her early life, Savannah is given
many cuddly toys when it is her birthday.
She keeps all her cuddly toys.

The table below shows how many cuddly
toys she has in total when she reaches
each birthday.

Birthday	1	2	3	4	5	6	7
Number of cuddly toys	3	5	8	12	17		

(a) The above pattern continues. How many cuddly toys will she have on
birthday 6?

(b) On which birthday will she have a total of 47 cuddly toys?

A   ALGEBRA 2EXT

1 Two of the inequalities below give possible x-values shown on the number lines beneath them. Match up the inequality with the correct number line and state clearly which inequality has no number line shown.

   Ⓐ $3x + 7 \leqslant 13$ Ⓑ $\dfrac{x}{2} > 2$ Ⓒ $5x - 3 \leqslant 2$

2 Jamie has to make x the subject of the formula $\dfrac{ax - c}{4} = m$

   His working out is shown below:

$$\frac{ax - c}{4} = m$$

$$\frac{ax}{4} = m + c$$

$$ax = 4(m + c)$$

$$x = \frac{4(m + c)}{a}$$

   Is Jamie correct? If not, explain any mistakes clearly.

3 Tickets for a dancing competition are sold at £9 for an adult and £5 for a child.
On the Friday night ticket sales amount to £715 and the total number of people who attend the competition is 95.
How many adults go to the competition on the Friday night?

> **Hint:**
> Let x = number of adults and y = number of children.
> The money means that $9x + 5y = 715$.
> Form another equation from the information.
> Now solve the simultaneous equations.

4   What value of x works for both the equation $x^2 - 2x - 15 = 0$ and for the equation $x^2 - 9x + 20 = 0$?

5   A sequence of patterns made from dots is shown below:

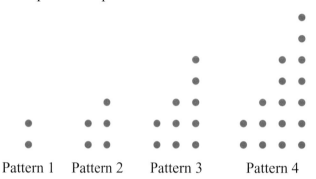

Pattern 1   Pattern 2   Pattern 3   Pattern 4

Does a pattern made with 82 dots fit this sequence?
You must give clear reasons for your answer.

6

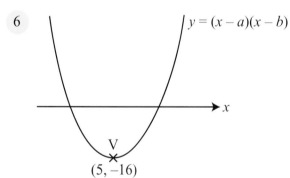

$y = (x - a)(x - b)$

(5, −16)

V

The vertex V is the minimum point of the curve shown.

The curve crosses the x-axis at $x = 1$.

(a) Write down the values of a and b.

(b) Multiply out the brackets to express the equation of the curve in the form $y = x^2 + mx + n$ where m and n are to be found.

7   A straight line has equation $y = 4x - 1$.

Does the line pass through the point (2, 5)?

You must justify your answer fully.

8 Nathan buys 5 razors and 2 shaving brushes for £9.30.

Kevin buys 9 razors and 3 shaving brushes for £15.30.

Work out the cost of each razor and each shaving brush.

Hint:
Let x be the cost of 1 razor and y be the cost of 1 shaving brush.

Form simultaneous equations then solve them.

9 The nth term of a sequence is $n^2 - 3n$.

Is 18 a number in the sequence?

Explain your answer fully.

10

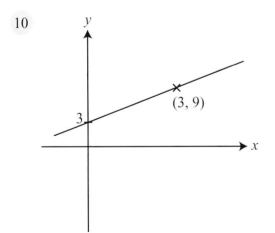

Does this line pass through the point (5, 13)?

Give full reasons for your answer.

11 Max is driving his car.

The graph below shows how his velocity increases steadily over a period of 20 seconds.

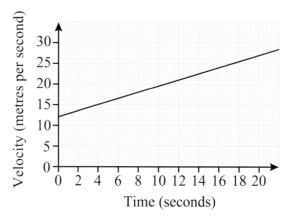

(a) Work out the rate at which the velocity increases over the 20 second period.

(b) Write down the word which usually describes the rate at which velocity changes.

> **Hint:**
> Rate of change = gradient

12 Find the co-ordinates of the point of intersection of the two lines $3x + 2y = 4$ and $4x - 3y = 11$.
Do not draw the graphs.

> **Hint:**
> Solve the equations simultaneously.

1 Tara runs a fruit and vegetable stall. She buys her apples from a local farm. The probability of an apple being rotten is 0.08

If she buys 175 apples from the farm, explain the calculation she must do in order to work out how many rotten apples she might expect to get.

2 50 people are asked if they go to the gym, jog or do neither.

(a) Copy and complete the Venn diagram below using the given information.

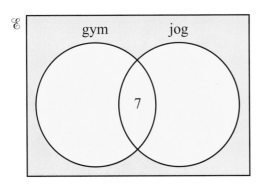

27 people jog and
21 people go to the gym.

(b) If one person is chosen at random, what is the probability that the person does not go to the gym or jog?

3 The only numbers on a dice are 6, 4 or 2.
The dice is thrown once.
The probability of throwing a 6 is three times greater than the probability of throwing a 2.
What is the probability of throwing a 4?

4   A hairdresser records how long people's appointments take during the month
of February. The information is shown below.

Time (to nearest minute)	0 to 15	16 to 20	21 to 25	26 to 30	over 30
Number of people	32	42	124	73	29

(a) What is the probability that a person with a hair appointment would need
16 to 20 minutes?

(b) 500 people come to the hairdresser during March.
How many of these people would you expect to need 16 to 20 minutes?

5   Martina is the world champion badminton player.
Ella started playing badminton one month ago.
Ella plays two games against Martina in a badminton match.
Ella will either win, draw or lose. She says the probability of her winning is $\frac{1}{3}$.
Explain why this is not correct.

6   Jaden found out which colour
straws had been used in a
restaurant during Thursday
evening. The findings are
shown in the tally chart below.

Colour	Tally
Blue	卌 卌 ||
Yellow	卌 |||
Red	卌 卌 ||||
White	||||
Purple	卌 卌 |
Green	卌 ||

(a) Draw a suitable chart or diagram to show Jaden's findings.

(b) How many straws were used in total during Thursday evening?

(c) Mackenzie went to the restaurant on Thursday evening and had a glass
of coke. What is the probability that she had a purple straw?

7   The frequency tree below shows where a group of 240 people went on holiday and whether they stayed in a hotel or went self-catering.

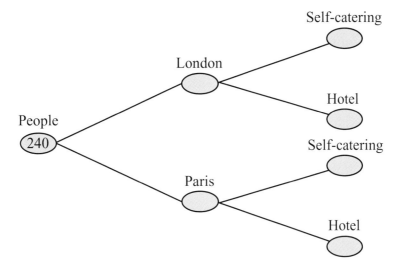

30% of the people went to London and the rest went to Paris.
50% of the people who went to Paris stayed in a hotel.
Overall 108 people stayed in a hotel.

(a) Copy and complete the frequency tree.

(b) What fraction of the people who went to London stayed in a hotel?

8   Brooke went to her local ice skating centre.
She randomly asked 25 people for their ages.
These ages are shown in the stem and leaf diagram below.

```
0 | 7 8 8
1 | 2 5 5 6 6 7 9
2 | 1 2 2 4 7
3 | 2 4 5 5 9
4 | 3 6 6 7
5 | 2
```

Key 2|4 means
24 years old

Hint:
e.g. 2|1 2 2 4 7
means the ages of
five people are
21, 22, 22, 24 and 27.

(a) What was the probability that a person chosen would be more than 40 years old?

(b) There were a total of 100 people in the ice skating centre.
How many of these people were likely to have been more than 40 years old?

9   Adam, Kaylee and Megan throw a coin many times.
The table below shows how many heads and tails they obtained.

	Adam	Kaylee	Megan
Heads	9	13	4
Tails	31	127	22

(a) Is this a 'fair' coin? Give a reason for your answer.

(b) Why might Kaylee's results give the most reliable data for working out the probability of getting heads with this coin?

10   Louise has four favourite ice cream flavours.
The probability of her choosing each of them is shown in the table below.

Flavour	Chocolate	Vanilla	Strawberry	Mint
Probability	0.25	n	n	0.05

(a) What is the probability of Louise choosing vanilla ice cream?

(b) What is the probability of Louise choosing vanilla or chocolate?

(c) During the next 20 times that Louise chooses ice cream, how often would you expect her to choose mint?

> **Hint:**
> The probabilities in the table must add up to 1.

11   There is a 0.78 chance that an insurance claim made to the 'Magpie Insurance Company' will be a car claim.
The car claim probability for the 'Denver Firm' is 0.6.

During November the 'Magpie Insurance Company' receive 350 insurance claims and the 'Denver Firm' receive 440 insurance claims.

Which firm gets the most car claims and by how many?

12 The Venn diagram below shows whether 100 young people do ballet, gymnastics or neither.

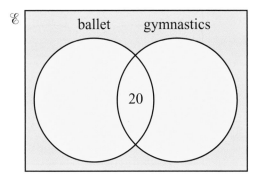

60 people do ballet and 28 people do neither.

If one person is chosen at random, what is the probability that the person does gymnastics?

1 In the Venn diagram opposite, which is greater:

$$n(A') \quad \text{or} \quad n(B')?$$

Explain your answer fully, stating the difference between the two values.

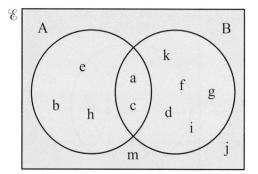

Hint:
$n(A)$ means the number of elements in set A. Each member of a set is called an element.

2 If events A and B are independent, the probability of A *and* B = probability of A × probability of B.

Write down what the two independent events A and B might be.
Explain why they are independent.

3 The Venn diagram below shows how many people competed for a country in the 2008 (A) Olympics then in the 2012 (B) Olympics.

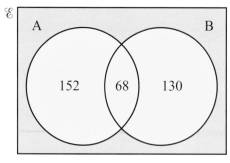

If a person is chosen at random, find

(a) the probability of A ∩ B, written $p(A \cap B)$

(b) $p(B')$

(c) $p(A' \cup B)$

4 Two spinners have the digits 1, 2, 3 and 4 on them.
   After each spin, the digits on each spinner are added together.
   Work out the probability that the
   total score is:

   (a) exactly 5

   (b) more than 6

   (c) Is the total score more likely
       to be a 3 or a 7?
       Justify your answer.

> **Hint:**
> Draw a table to show all the
> possible scores that could
> be found.

5 A coin and a dice are thrown. The probability tree below shows the outcomes
   for heads, tails, even numbers and odd numbers.

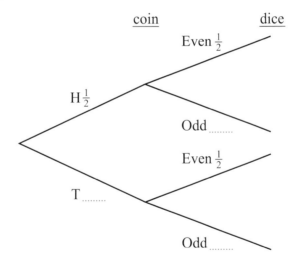

   (a) Copy and complete the probability tree.

   (b) Work out the probability that the coin will land on tails and the dice will
       show an odd number.

6 The probability of passing a test is $\frac{4}{5}$.

   Jack fails the test on his first attempt then passes on his second attempt.
   Work out the probability of this happening.

7   200 people are asked if they regularly carry water with them. They are also asked if they get a headache at all during the day. The information is shown in the frequency tree below.

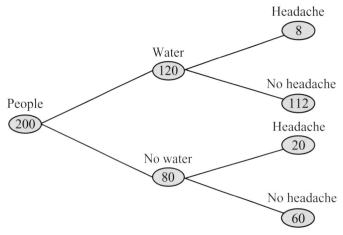

(a) If one person is chosen at random, what is the probability that the person gets a headache?

(b) If the person carried water, what is the probability that the person did not get a headache?

8   The probability tree opposite is drawn to represent a situation. a, b, c, d, e, f and g are probabilities.

Explain clearly why
$a + b = c + d + e = f + g = 1$

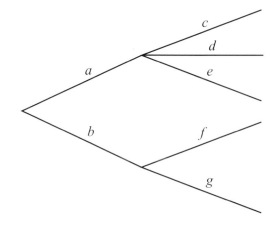

9 There are 16 blue or red fish in a tank. The ratio of blue to red fish is 5 : 3.
   Another tank contains three times as many blue or red fish.
   The ratio of blue to red fish is 2 : 1.
   All the fish are put together in a large tank.
   If one fish is removed at random from this large tank, what is the probability of
   this fish being blue?

10 There are 20 cats in a cattery
    of which 9 are black.

    Work out the probability that
    the first two cats to leave the
    cattery will be black.

11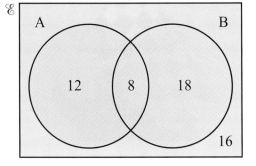

    Explain *fully* why
    $p((A \cup B)') = \frac{8}{27}$

12 Leah keeps throwing 3 coins.
    If she does this 50 times, how many times would you expect the coins to land
    on 3 heads at the same time?

M | MIXED 4A

1   Mr. and Mrs. Jenkins stay at the Melton Hotel for a short holiday. They go on a Monday and stay for four nights in a double room.

They have evening dinner in the hotel on Monday and Wednesday only.

Mr. and Mrs. Jenkins get a 15% discount on the rooms only by

MELTON HOTEL	
	room cost per night
double room (Mon–Thu)	£130
double room (Fri–Sun)	£150
single room (Mon–Thu)	£105
single room (Fri–Sun)	£115
evening dinner £28.50 per person	

booking the holiday through Starlight Travel Company. How much do they pay in total for the room and evening dinners?

2   Ella says that the value of $3a^2$ is 12 when $a = -2$.
Explain in detail how Ella obtained this answer.

3   Dylan and five friends want to watch either motorcycle racing or go-karting. The motorcycle racing costs £15.50 per person and is six miles from Dylan's house. The go-karting costs £12.50 per person and is nine miles from Dylan's house. The local taxi firm charges the following:

Cab for four people	£2.70 per mile
Cab for nine people	£5.50 per mile

Hint:
Think carefully about how the 6 people choose their taxis.

Dylan and his friends wish to go by taxi. They choose the event which will cost them the least money for entry to the event and a taxi there and back to Dylan's house. How much cheaper per person is this choice?

4 Larry, Jake and Josh play for the same football team.
Last season Larry scored 6 goals more than Jake.
Larry scored three times as many goals
as Josh.
They scored 43 goals between them.
How many goals did each of them
score?

Hint:
Let n be the number of
goals scored by Josh. Form
an algebraic equation then
solve it.

5

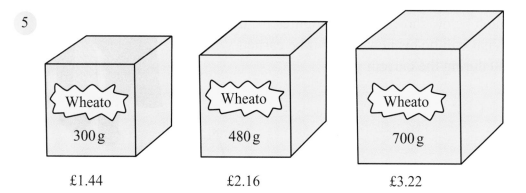

£1.44   £2.16   £3.22

The prices of three different sized boxes of cereal are shown above.

Which box offers the best value for money?
You must show all your working out.

6

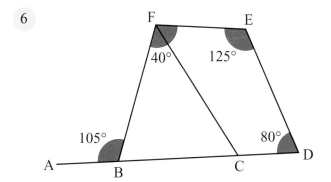

Calculate the size of angle CFE.

You must give reasons for each
step in your working.

Hint:
The angles in a
quadrilateral add
up to 360°.

7　Some theatre ticket prices are shown opposite.

Some friends go to see a show and spend a total of £172.30.

If three of the friends bought Circle tickets, how many of them bought Stall tickets?

MERLIN THEATRE PRICES	
Stall	£26.20
Circle	£22.50

8　Chase sells computers. He has been promised a 12% pay increase if he sells at least 100 computers during the year. The increase will be 15% if he sells at least 120 computers during the year. The graph below shows his sales figures for the year. What will be his new salary if he earned £16 200 during the current year?

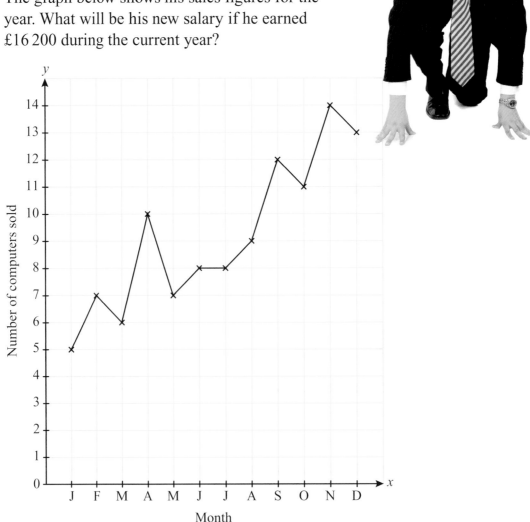

9

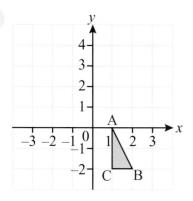

Evelyn is asked to translate a triangle with the vector $\begin{pmatrix} -2 \\ -3 \end{pmatrix}$.

She makes a mistake and translates the triangle with vector $\begin{pmatrix} 2 \\ -3 \end{pmatrix}$.

Her answer is shown opposite.
Where should the final triangle have been?
(Use your own diagram then write down the co-ordinates of the vertices of the correct final triangle.)

10   $\mathscr{E}$ = {students in Year 11}
   G = {students who study Geography}
   H = {students who study History}

75 out of the 200 students in Year 11 do not study Geography or History.
95 students study Geography and 75 students study History.

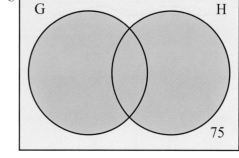

By copying and completing the Venn diagram, work out how many students studied both Geography and History.

11   In house A the floor area covered by carpet compared to non-carpet is in the ratio 5 : 3. In house B the floor area covered by carpet compared to non-carpet is in the ratio 3 : 2.

   (a) For each house, write down what fraction of the floor area is covered by carpet.

   (b) In which house is the greater proportion of the floor area covered by carpet? Explain fully how you made the comparison.

12 Colin and five friends want to go to
Athens for a short holiday. Colin
finds the deal below on the internet.

| Athens £470 per person for 4 nights |
| 10% off for groups of six people or more |
| 15% off for groups of eight people or more |

Special September offer:
20% discount on the price of the holiday
if you travel in September.

What will be the total cost of
the holiday for Colin and the
five friends if they travel in
September?

M | MIXED 4EXT

1 Payton drives from Glastonbury to Moreton-in-Marsh and back again.
The reading on her speedometer before and after is shown below.

Before	57874

After	58060

Her car does 31 miles on one gallon of petrol. The cost of petrol is shown below.

£6.98 per gallon

How much does it cost Payton to drive from Glastonbury to Moreton-in-Marsh and back again?

2 Prove that $(x - 2)(4x + 10) \equiv (2x - 4)(2x + 5)$.

> **Hint:**
> '$\equiv$' means 'is identical to'. This means it is true for all values of x.

3 80 people were asked whether they like Coronation Street or Eastenders.

8 people said they like Coronation Street only.

20 people said they like Eastenders only.

30 people said they do not like either.

(a) Complete a Venn diagram for the above information

(b) If one person is chosen at random, what is the probability of the person liking both Coronation Street and Eastenders.

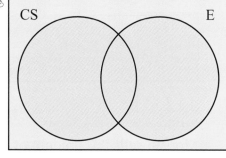

(c) Given that a person likes Eastenders, what is the probability that the person likes Coronation Street also?

4

Tax allowance
£11 000

Income Tax
20%

The tax allowance is the amount of money a person may earn before paying income tax on the remaining money.

A person pays 20% of the remaining money as income tax.

Huo earns £16 000 for the year and Kevin earns £14 500.

How much more income tax must Huo pay than Kevin?

5

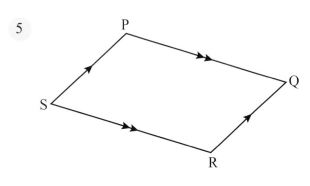

$\overrightarrow{SR} = \begin{pmatrix} 7 \\ -2 \end{pmatrix}$ and $\overrightarrow{RQ} = \begin{pmatrix} 3 \\ 5 \end{pmatrix}$

PQRS is a parallelogram.

(a) Explain clearly why $\overrightarrow{SQ} = \begin{pmatrix} 10 \\ 3 \end{pmatrix}$

(b) Express $\overrightarrow{SP}$ as a column vector.

(c) Express $\overrightarrow{QP}$ as a column vector.

(d) Express $\overrightarrow{RP}$ as a column vector.

6 Morgan sells wine. She receives 20% commission on any wine that she sells. Last week she travelled from York to Sheffield then to Nottingham then back to York. She can claim 21.5p travel expenses for every mile that she covers.

The distances between certain places are shown below.

York				
58	Sheffield			
87	35	Derby		
82	28	7	Nottingham	
25	40	74	67	Leeds

Morgan sells this amount of wine in each place.

(Sheffield £320)   (Nottingham £794)   (York £283)

How much money does Morgan get in total from her wine commission and travel expenses?

7

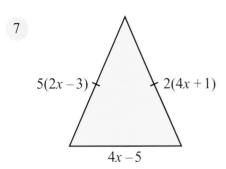

$5(2x-3)$ $2(4x+1)$

$4x-5$

The triangle opposite is isosceles and the lengths are given in centimetres.

Work out the value of x then write down the actual perimeter of the triangle.

8

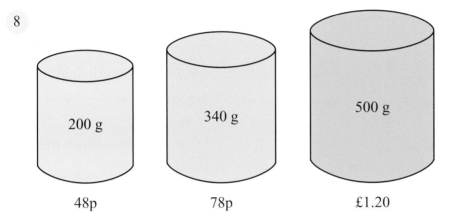

200 g

340 g

500 g

48p

78p

£1.20

The prices of three tins of baked beans are shown above.
Which tin gives the best value? Explain your answer fully.

9

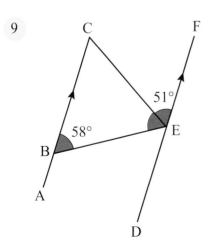

The lines AC and DF are parallel.
Calculate the value of angle BEC.
Give reasons for your answer.

10 One day Suraj sees 4 types of bird.

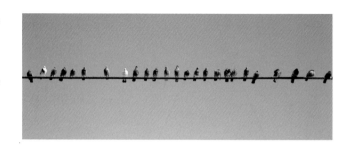

80% of the birds are starlings. The remaining birds are pigeons, bluetits and magpies in the ratio 7 : 3 : 2.

If Suraj sees 15 bluetits, how many starlings does he see?

11 There is a 58% chance that a seventeen-year-old has a GCSE Maths grade of 5 or above.

There is a 66% chance that a seventeen-year-old has a GCSE English grade of 5 or above.

If a seventeen-year-old is chosen at random, what is the probability that this person will have a grade 5 or above in Maths or English but not both?

Hint:
Draw a probability tree.

Maths   English

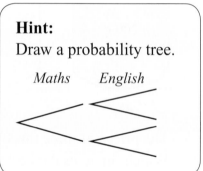

12 Robert, Arjun and Zoe each invest £3000 in shares.
The value of their money rises or falls each year as shown below.

Robert	
Year 1	rises 5%
Year 2	drops 2%

Arjun	
Year 1	drops 3%
Year 2	rises 6%

Zoe	
Year 1	rises 2%
Year 2	rises 1%

The percentage change each year is a percentage of the amount of money at the start of the year.
Which person has the most money after two years?
Show your working out fully.

How much money do Robert, Arjun and Zoe have in total after two years?

G | GEOMETRY 2A

1

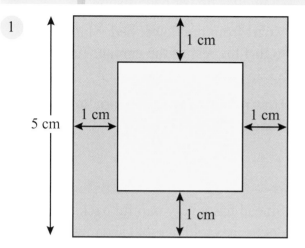

Each side of the large square has length 5 cm.

Work out the area of the grey border.

Hint:
Find the area of the small square inside first.

2 Brandon lays 150 bricks in one hour. On Tuesday he has a 20 minute morning break and a 45 minute lunch break. He starts work at 8 a.m. and has to lay 900 bricks.

At what time should Brandon finish laying all these bricks?

3

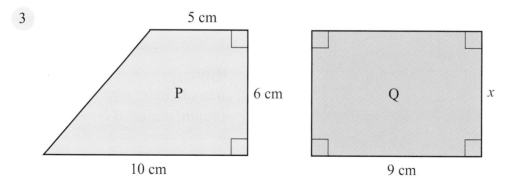

Find the length x if the area of shape P is equal to the area of shape Q.

4

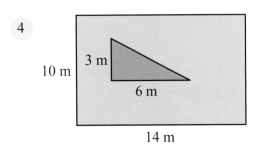

Maria has a rectangular garden with a triangular flower bed as shown.

Apart from the flower bed. Maria wants to turf the rest of the garden. Turf costs £3.25 per square metre.

How much will it cost Maria to lay turf in her garden?

5

Item	Weight
Bag of sugar	500 g
Apples	820 g
Bag of plain flour	1 kg
Cheese	370 g
Potatoes	4.2 kg
Carrots	585 g

Sinead has a very painful back. Her doctor has told her that she must not carry more than 7.5 kg of items.

Can Sinead safely carry all her shopping shown in the table opposite?

Explain your answer fully.

6

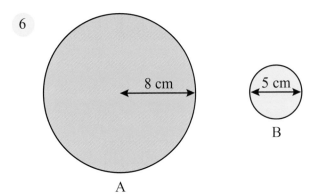

A

B

Circle A has radius 8 cm.
Circle B has diameter 5 cm.

Express the area of circle B as a percentage of the area of circle A. Give your answer to one decimal place.

Hint:
area of circle $= \pi r^2$
circumference of circle $= \pi d$

7   A small box of chocolates measures
10 cm by 10 cm by 10 cm as shown.

Some of these small boxes of chocolates
are packed into a large box which measures
30 cm × 20 cm × 21 cm.

As many small boxes as possible are
packed into the large box. What is the
total value of these small boxes if
one small box of chocolates costs
£5.99?

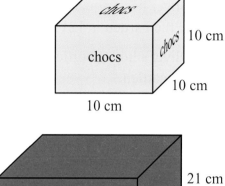

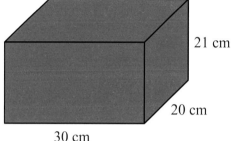

8   The departure times of some trains from York to Birmingham New Street are
shown below.

York			0757	0830	0930	1057	1130	1157
Sheffield			0857	0930	1030	1157	1230	1257
Chesterfield			0921	0954	1054	1221	1254	1321
Derby			0943	1016	1116	1243	1316	1343
Burton			1016	1049	1149	1316	1349	1416
Birmingham New Street			1042	1115	1215	1342	1415	1442

Huan leaves a hotel in York at 0745. It takes her 20 minutes to get to the train
station.
She gets on the first possible train to Derby.

She gets off the train at Derby to do some shopping but must catch a train to
Birmingham New Street in time to meet a friend there at 2:45 p.m.

What is the greatest amount of time that Huan can spend in Derby?

9 Oliver has a square garden. The area
   of the garden is 121 m².

   Oliver's house borders one side of
   the garden.
   The rest of the garden has fencing around
   the edge apart from a 1.5 m wide gate.

   What is the total length of fencing used
   for his garden?

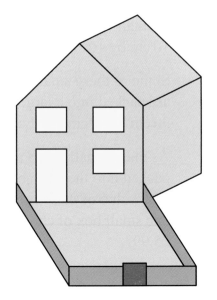

10

Paint
1 *l*

£10.50

Paint
2.5 *l*

£18.50

Paint
5 *l*

£38.50

Makayla wants to paint 3 walls in a room as shown below.

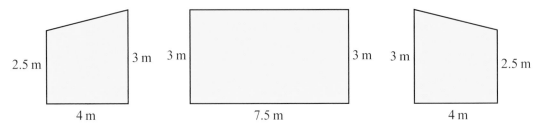

2.5 m   3 m   3 m   3 m   3 m   2.5 m

4 m   7.5 m   4 m

If 1 litre of paint will cover an area of 6 m², which tins of paint must Makayla
buy so that she pays the least amount of money?

Give full reasons for your answer.

11 A plane travels 150 miles in 15 minutes.

Mackenzie works out the speed using the $\triangle$ triangle.

She writes '*speed* $= \dfrac{distance}{time} = \dfrac{150}{15} = 10\ miles\ per\ hour$'.

Mackenzie is not happy with her answer. What has she done wrong?

12 Arushi reads her gas meter at the start of September.
The dials below show the reading.

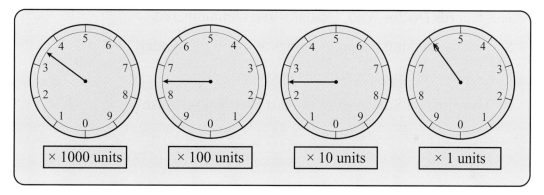

She reads the meter again at the start of December.
The dials below show the reading.

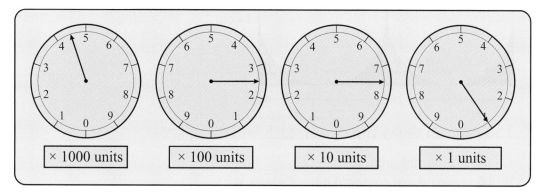

Arushi must pay 16.8p per unit for the first 220 units she has used.

She pays 12.4p per unit for the rest of the units she has used.

How much must she pay in total for this gas bill?

G | GEOMETRY 2B

1 The times of some Saturday evening programmes are shown below.

19:05	Doctor Who
19:55	In it to win it
20:45	Casualty
21:40	Outnumbered
22:10	News
22:25	Match of the Day

Jess records Doctor Who, Casualty and Outnumbered.

She starts watching the programmes at 14:15 on Sunday.

She watches all the programmes in one go.

At what time on Sunday does the last programme finish?

2

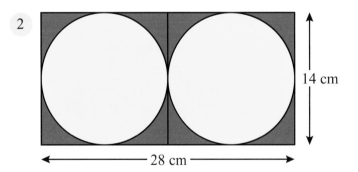

This diagram shows two circles, each inside a square.

Calculate the red area.
(Give your answer to one decimal place.)

3 Yakov is making jelly in two types of mould.
   One mould is a cuboid and one mould is a prism as shown below.

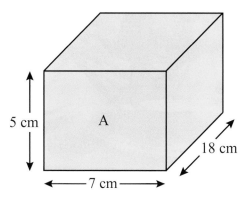

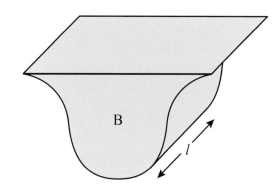

The volume of jelly in each mould is the same.
If the front cross-sectional area of mould B
is 70 cm², find the length *l* of mould B.

Hint:
volume of prism = area
of cross-section × length

4 Carson's mother wants him back home by 7:45 p.m. for a meal.
   Carson is at a friend's house. Carson wants to play squash before going home
   and needs to visit a local store to buy some chocolates. Look at the table below
   and work out the latest time he can leave his friend's house so that he gets back
   home in time for the meal.

Walk from friend's house to squash court	25 minutes
Change for squash	5 minutes
Play squash	45 minutes
Clean and change into normal clothes	10 minutes
Walk from squash court to store	15 minutes
Buy chocolates	10 minutes
Walk from store to home	20 minutes

5 A single record is a circular
disc of diameter 17.5 cm.
A piece of fluff is resting
on the edge of the record.
The record is played at 45 rpm
(45 revolutions per minute)
– this means that the record
turns 45 full circles in one
minute.

How many metres does the
piece of fluff travel in one minute?
Give the answer to one decimal place.

6

Uma wants to tile three walls in her kitchen.

One wall is a rectangle of length 2.8 m and width 2.25 m.
The other two walls are each of length 3.2 m and width 2.25 m.

Each rectangular tile has length 25 cm and width 20 cm.

Uma can buy the tiles in boxes of 30.
She buys one extra box to allow for mistakes
when tiling.
Each box of tiles costs £31.20.

How much does Uma pay for all the tiles?

7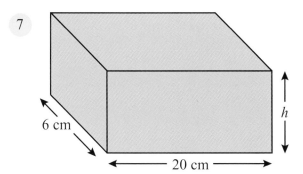

This cuboid has volume 480 cm^3.

It has length 20 cm, width 6 cm and height h cm.

Work out the total surface area of the cuboid.

Give the answer in cm^2.

8 During one evening a restaurant makes and sells 10.5 litres of coffee.

250 ml of coffee is used for each cup.

One cup of coffee costs £2.30.

Find the total amount of money the restaurant receives for selling coffee during that evening.

9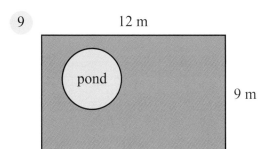

The diagram opposite shows the garden of a new house which has just been built.

The pond has radius 2 m.

The builder needs to put topsoil on the rest of the garden. The topsoil will be 0.4 m deep.

What volume of topsoil will the builder need to use? Give the answer to the nearest m^3.

10 Car A is travelling at 54 km/h and car B is travelling at 16 m/s.
Pete says that car B is travelling faster than car A.
Explain clearly whether Pete is correct or not.

11 The chart below shows some train times.

Westbury	1542	1619	1719	1758	1837	1920
Trowbridge	1551	1628	1728	1807	1846	1929
Bath	1601	1638	1738	1817	1856	1939
Bristol	1620	1658	1758	1836	1915	1958

Bristol	2018	2047	2118	2207	2218	2305
Bath	2036	2105	2136	2225	2236	2323
Trowbridge	2046	2115	2146	2235	2246	2333
Westbury	2057	2126	2157	2246	2257	2344

Natalia lives in Westbury. It takes her 20 minutes to walk from her home to Westbury train station. It takes her 25 minutes to get from Bristol train station to the Hippodrome.

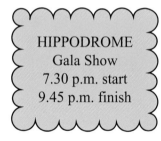

HIPPODROME
Gala Show
7.30 p.m. start
9.45 p.m. finish

(a) What is the latest time that she can leave home so that she can get to the Hippodrome for the start of the Gala Show?

(b) Natalia catches the earliest possible train after the Gala Show back to Westbury. How long is it in total between her leaving home and arriving back home?

12 A glass in the shape of a cylinder has radius 3.5 cm. It is filled with lemonade to a height of 6 cm.

Carly's parents fill 50 glasses in this way for a party.

They buy the lemonade in one litre bottles.

How many bottles of lemonade do they need?

(Reminder: 1 litre = 1000 cm³)

Hint:
volume of a cylinder $= \pi r^2 \times$ height

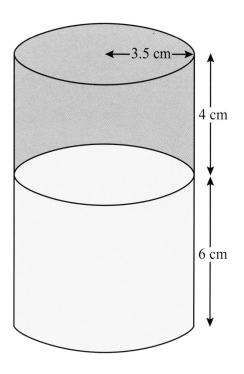

1

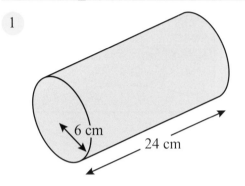

Ruby melts down a metal cylinder of radius 6 cm as shown. She makes as many cubes as possible from the metal.

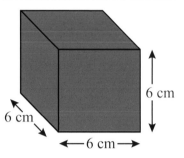

Each cube measures 6 cm by 6 cm by 6 cm.

How many cubes does Ruby make?

Show all your working out fully.

2   A large house has a drive in front of it as shown opposite.

The diagram shows a smaller semi-circle inside a larger semi-circle.

The drive is to be covered with gravel.

There are two types of gravel available as shown in the table below.

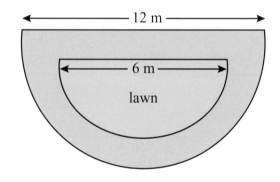

One tonne of gravel A	One tonne of gravel B
Covers $17\,\text{m}^2$	Covers $12\,\text{m}^2$
Costs £148	Costs £106

The gravel can only be bought in multiples of tonnes.

Which gravel will be cheaper to use and by how much?

3   Martin truncates the weight of a pencil sharpener to 1 decimal place so he gives the weight as 31.6 g.

(a) Write down an inequality for the possible weight of the pencil sharpener.

(b) Martin buys 700 pencil sharpeners identical to the one above. He says that their total weight is $700 \times 31.6 = 22\,120\,\text{g}$.
Jade says that the pencil sharpeners could weigh up to 70 g more than this.
Explain in detail why Jade says this.

4

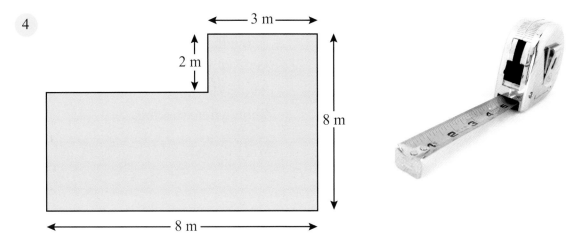

Ayden wants to carpet the room shown above. Any carpet he buys will be 6 m wide. He only wants one line where two pieces of carpet join together. The carpet costs £25 per square metre.

What is the least amount Ayden will have to spend to carpet the entire room? Explain your working out fully.

5

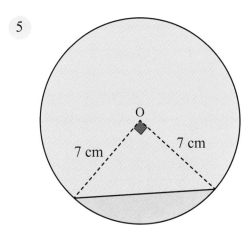

A circular piece of pastry has a small segment cut from it (the grey area shown opposite).

Calculate the percentage of the original piece of pastry which remains, giving your answer to one decimal place.

Hint:
To express the number m as a percentage of the number n, work out $\dfrac{m}{n} \times 100\%$

6

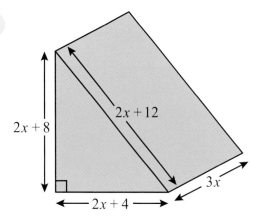
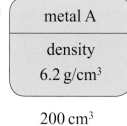

The diagram shows a prism.
Show that the volume of the prism
is given by the expression
$6x^3 + 36x^2 + 48x$

Show your working.

7

metal A	metal B
density	density
6.2 g/cm^3	7.8 g/cm^3

200 cm^3 300 cm^3

The two metals are melted down and
made into a single piece of metal alloy.
Explain in detail why the density of
the metal alloy is 7.16 g/cm^3.

Hint:

$$\text{Density} = \frac{\text{Mass}}{\text{Volume}}$$

8   The cardboard box opposite measures
$100 \text{ cm} \times 75 \text{ cm} \times 55 \text{ cm}$.

Julian has 80 packets with the
dimensions $25 \text{ cm} \times 25 \text{ cm} \times 10 \text{ cm}$.

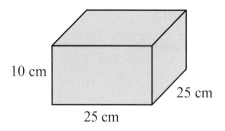

Julian puts as many packets as possible into the cardboard box and seals it.
How many packets are left over?

9   The volume of the cube opposite is $1\,m^3$.
     Gabriella says that $1\,m^3 = 100\,cm^3$.

     (a) Use the cube opposite to explain
         why Gabriella is wrong.

     (b) Convert $5\,m^3$ into cm^3.

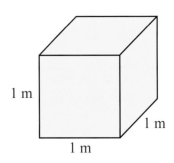

1 m

1 m

1 m

10   A shop sells rolls of carpets which are wide
     enough for Eric's rectangular bedroom.
     The carpet can be bought in lengths as
     shown in the table opposite.

     Eric measures the length of his bedroom
     as 11 feet.
     He must convert this into metres to decide
     which length of carpet to buy.

Carpet length	Cost
2.5 m	£128
3 m	£153.60
3.5 m	£179.20
4 m	£204.80
4.5 m	£230.40
5 m	£256
5.5 m	£281.60
6 m	£307.20

     Using the information shown opposite,
     what is the least amount of money
     Eric can spend to carpet his bedroom?

1 inch	= 2.5 cm
1 foot	= 12 inches
1 kg	= 2.2 pounds
1 litre	= 1.8 pints

11   The triangular metal prism opposite stands
     on a table and has a weight of 288 N.
     The prism can stand on any of its 5 faces.
     On which face would it stand when
     exerting the greatest pressure on the table.
     You must fully justify your answer.

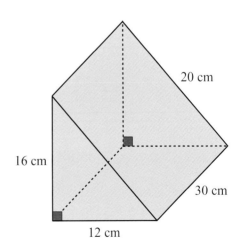

20 cm

16 cm

30 cm

12 cm

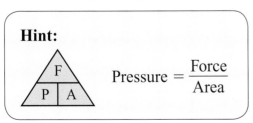

Hint:

F	
P	A

$$\text{Pressure} = \frac{\text{Force}}{\text{Area}}$$

12

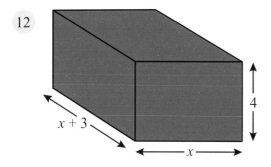

$x + 3$

x

4

All measurements shown on the cuboid opposite are given in metres.
The volume of the cuboid is $216\,\text{m}^3$.

(a) Explain fully why $x^2 + 3x - 54 = 0$

(b) Write down the actual dimensions of this cuboid.

S STATISTICS 2A

1   Blake and Stella play a game of darts.
    Their scores with each set of three darts
    is shown below.

Blake: 40	27	8	78	55	58
60	60	52	23	40	

Stella: 26	41	60	60	37
29	52	39	34	58

Compare fully the scores for
Blake and Stella.

Hint:

To compare 2 sets of data, you must
compare an average (mean, median or
mode) and the spread of the data (range).

2   Luis has 3 cards each with a positive whole number written on it.

The median of the three numbers is 4.

The mean of the three numbers is 5.

(a) Work out the three numbers on the cards.

(b) There are four possible answers to part (a)

    Find all four possible sets of numbers.

3 125 students in year 9 study French, German or Spanish.
22 girls study French. There are 70 girls in total.
25 boys do German. There are 42 students doing Spanish, of which 12 are boys.

How many students in total study German?

Hint:
Draw a two-way table.

	French	German	Spanish	Total
Boys		25	12	
Girls	22		30	70
Total			42	125

Now work out the empty spaces to find the answer to the question.

4 Write down a question which may have
been used in a survey to give the
frequency table shown below:

Animal	Number of people
Lion	58
Elephant	91
Leopard	32
Giraffe	68
Kangaroo	47

5 The range of the numbers below is 16.

25   29   32   33   ?

Write down the two possible values for the unknown number.

6 Juan visits Chicago in the USA. His grandparents give him an extra £170 to spend. The graph below can be used to convert between £(pounds) and $(dollars).

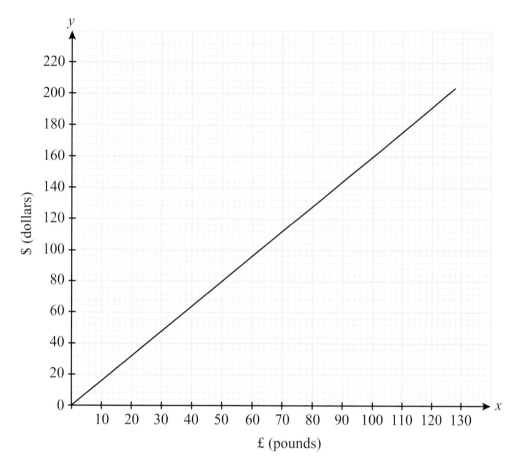

In Chicago Juan buys a jacket for $112, a baseball hat for $24 and a rucksack for $136.

How much money does he have left from his grandparents' money?

You must show all your working.

7 The pie charts below show the proportion of people who play hockey, tennis and squash at two sports clubs.

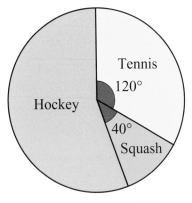

Whitstone Sports Club

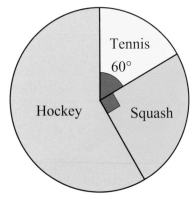

Hatton Sports Club

6 people play squash at Whitstone Sports Club and 30 people play squash at Hatton Sports Club.

Evie says that 'more people play tennis at Hatton Sports Club than at Whitstone Sports Club'.

Is she correct or not? Give full reasons for your answer.

8 160 tourists to London are asked what their favourite sights are. They all choose Buckingham Palace, Tower Bridge, Big Ben or the Tower of London.

10 of the 85 women choose Tower Bridge.

7 men choose Big Ben.

$\frac{3}{4}$ of the 60 people who choose the Tower of London are men.

70% of the 70 people who choose Buckingham Palace are women.

Find the total number of tourists who choose Big Ben.

9 Murray throws a dice 40 times. His scores are shown
in the frequency table below.

Score	Frequency
1	10
2	8
3	6
4	7
5	7
6	2

Calculate Murray's mean score.

Hint:
Remember that the table tells us
that he threw the score 1 ten times
and the score 2 eight times, etc.

10 Some people are asked for information about themselves regarding:

number of GCSEs above grade 3   shoe size

height   hair colour   time to run 100 metres

Identify two of the above which could
be used to create a scatter graph which
shows positive correlation.
Justify your choice.

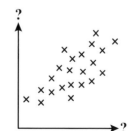

11   90 people are asked what their
     favourite form of transport is.
     The information is shown in
     the table below.

Form of transport	Frequency
Car	8
Boat	20
Plane	14
Bike	16
Train	25
Other	7

Represent this information in a suitable diagram or chart.

12   An airport records the number of cases each passenger has.
     The results for the first 50 passengers are shown below:

2 1 1 3 1 0 2 2 1 3 3 0 1 1 0 1 2 3 4 2 1 3 1 1 2

3 1 0 0 2 2 2 1 0 3 1 1 2 0 1 1 1 2 1 4 0 1 1 2 2

(a) Copy and complete the frequency
    table.

(b) Calculate the total number of cases
    brought by these 50 passengers.

(c) Find the mean number of cases per
    passenger.

Number of cases	Frequency
0	
1	
2	
3	
4	

S | STATISTICS 2B

1 Sam has five cards each with a number on it as shown below.

| 4 | 5 | 7 | ? | ? |

Find the two missing numbers if the mode is 5 and the mean is 6.

2 Each week Lan has a Maths test and an English test.
The table below shows her marks (out of 20) for each test during one half term.

	Week 1	Week 2	Week 3	Week 4	Week 5	Week 6
Maths	14	13	16	16	15	17
English	11	14	12	11	13	12

Lan wants to compare her Maths marks with her English marks.
On squared paper, draw a suitable diagram or chart.

3 156 students in Hatton High School are asked which Science subject they liked best.

One third of the 90 boys chose Chemistry.

40% of the 60 students who chose Physics were girls.

27 girls chose Biology.

Find the total number of students who chose Biology.

Hint:
Make a two-way table.

4   Some people in Newcastle and Gloucester were asked if they own a dog.
    The information was used to draw the pie charts below which show the
    proportion of people who own a dog.

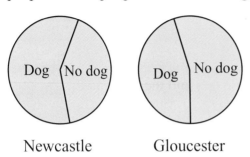

Newcastle   Gloucester

Charlie says that 'more people own a
dog in Newcastle than in Gloucester'.
Is he correct?
Justify your answer.

5   The bar chart below shows the monthly rainfall in Porto for the summer
    months. This table shows the monthly rainfall in Barcelona for the same
    months.

Month	May	June	July	Aug	Sep	Oct
Rainfall (mm)	40	35	15	20	35	55

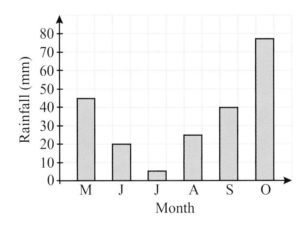

(a) Draw a suitable chart for Barcelona
    on a second set of axes.

(b) Compare the rainfall of the two
    cities.

Hint:
To compare 2 sets of data,
you must compare an average
(mean, median or mode) and
the spread of the data (range).

6   90 people were asked how they mostly exercise. They all said that they cycle, jog or go to the gym.

55 of the people were over 30 years old and seven of them chose 'jog'.

80% of the 50 people who chose 'gym' were over 30 years old.

20 people who chose 'cycle' were 30 years old or under.

How many people in total said they prefer to cycle?

7   A scatter graph shows negative correlation. Describe what this scatter graph will look like.

8   Twenty five children take a times table test. Their test marks are shown in the chart below.

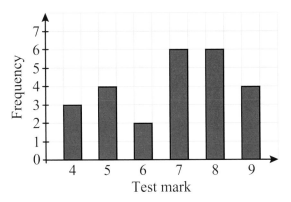

$1 \times 3 = 3$ $1 \times 4 = 4$ $1 \times 5 = 5$ $1 \times 6 = 6$
$2 \times 3 = 6$ $2 \times 4 = 8$ $2 \times 5 = 10$ $2 \times 6 = 12$
$3 \times 3 = 9$ $3 \times 4 = 12$ $3 \times 5 = 15$ $3 \times 6 = 18$
$4 \times 3 = 12$ $4 \times 4 = 16$ $4 \times 5 = 20$ $4 \times 6 = 24$
$5 \times 3 = 15$ $5 \times 4 = 20$ $5 \times 5 = 25$ $5 \times 6 = 30$
$6 \times 3 = 18$ $6 \times 4 = 24$ $6 \times 5 = 30$ $6 \times 6 = 36$
$7 \times 3 = 21$ $7 \times 4 = 28$ $7 \times 5 = 35$ $7 \times 6 = 42$
$8 \times 3 = 24$ $8 \times 4 = 32$ $8 \times 5 = 40$ $8 \times 6 =$
$9 \times 3 = 27$ $9 \times 4 = 36$ $9 \times 5 = 45$ $9 \times 6 =$
$10 \times 3 = 30$ $10 \times 4 = 40$ $10 \times 5 = 50$ $10 \times$
$11 \times 3 = 33$ $11 \times 4 = 44$ $11 \times 5 = 55$ $11 \times$
$12 \times 4 = 48$ $12 \times 5 = 60$ $12 \times$

(a) Calculate the mean test mark for these 25 children.

(b) Another child takes the test and scores a mark of 6.
     Will the new mean test mark for all 26 children be more or less than the mean test mark found in part (a)?
     Give a clear reason for your answer.

9 45 people were asked what their favourite athletics track event was.
The results are shown in the table below.

Event	Number of people
100 m	16
200 m	5
400 m	5
800 m	3
1500 m	12
5000 m	4

Represent this information in a suitable diagram or chart.

10 The weights of 16 footballers in a squad are given below (in kg).

Weight (W)	Frequency
$60 \leqslant W < 70$	5
$70 \leqslant W < 80$	7
$80 \leqslant W < 90$	3
$90 \leqslant W < 100$	1

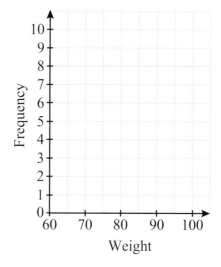

(a) Draw a suitable chart or graph to show these weights.

(b) Write down the modal interval for the weights.

(c) Work out an estimate for the mean weight of the footballers.

(d) An 80 kg footballer joins the squad.
What will happen to the value of the mean weight for the whole squad?
Give a reason for your answer.

11 A grocer measured the length of
16 bananas in one box (box A).
Each length is given below to
the nearest cm.

21   18   22   22   19   18   20   21

17   22   20   18   17   21   17   21

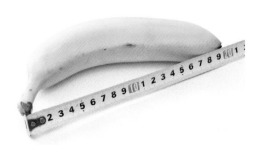

(a) Copy and complete the frequency
table for these bananas.

Length (cm)	Tally	Frequency
17		
18		
19		
20		
21		
22		

(b) Write down the mode, median and range of the length of the bananas.

(c) The grocer measures the lengths of some bananas from another box
(box B).

He works out the following:

mode = 16 cm   mean = 17.8 cm

median = 17 cm   range = 10 cm

Compare the lengths of the bananas in box A with the lengths of the
bananas in box B.

12 Hayden is in charge of bungee jumping
    for three months at a holiday resort
    in Australia.

    In the stem and leaf diagram below,
    Hayden records how many people bungee
    jump each week.

    0 | 8
    1 | 1 1 2 4 4 7 8
    2 | 1 3 3 3 6

    Key
    1|4 means 14 people

    Calculate

    (a) the mean number of people who
        bungee jump each week

    (b) the median number of people

    (c) the modal number of people

    (d) the range for the number of people.

    (e) An extra two weeks of bungee jumping is added on.
        22 people jump in the first week and 10 people jump in the second week.
        How does this change the median number of people for all the weeks?
        Give clear reasons for your answer.

1   Thirteen people went out to collect money for the charity 'Food Aid'.
    Fifteen people collected money for the charity 'Save the Whales'.
    The total amount collected by each person is shown in the back-to-back stem
    and leaf diagram.

Food Aid			Save the Whales
9 3	2	4 6
8 6 6	3	2 2 4 7 8
5 2	4	1 6 9
4 4 3	5	4
1	6	7 8
7 4	7	2 2

Key 5|4 = £45   Key 4|6 = £46

The Food Aid people need to raise at least £600 to help a village in Africa.
Do they collect enough money? You must show all your working out.

2   240 students in Grafton School were asked which Harry Potter book was their
    favourite. The results are shown in the first pie chart below.

    The same question is given to some students in the Madeley High School.
    70 students preferred Book 6.
    The results are shown in the second pie chart below.

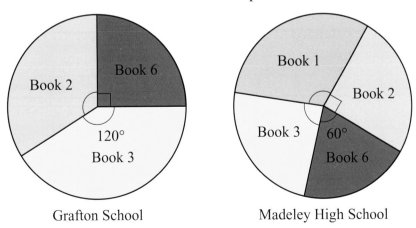

Grafton School   Madeley High School

In which school did more students prefer Book 2 and by how many?

3 A shoe shop records the heights and shoe sizes of a number of people.
The information is shown on the scatter graph below.

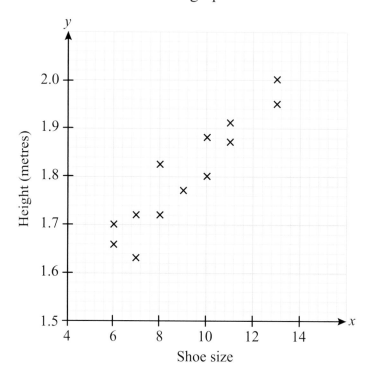

One more person of height 1.82 m has shoe size 11.

(a) Copy the scattergraph and mark on this final person.

(b) Describe the relationship between the shoe sizes and the heights of these people.

(c) Estimate the height of a person with shoe size 12.

(d) Could the graph be extended to estimate the shoe size of a person 1.3 m tall? Fully justify your answer.

Hint:
Draw a line of best fit.

4 30 people are asked which party they
   voted for at the last General Election.
   The information is shown in the bar
   chart opposite.
   Draw a pie chart to represent this
   information.

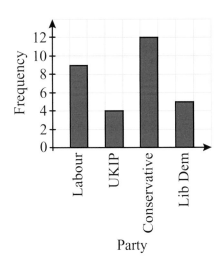

5 Ten people threw a dice.
   Their scores are shown in the bar chart below.

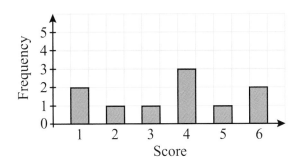

Which is larger – the mean score or the median score?
Write down the difference between them.

6 (a) Explain what a simple random sample is.

   (b) Anton and Natalia need to each gather a simple random sample from a
        group of people. Anton writes names on strips of paper of varying sizes.
        He then mixes them up in a box and chooses 10 strips.
        Natalia assigns a number to each person. Each number is placed on a
        separate ball then the balls are mixed up in a box. She then chooses 10 balls.
        (i)   Are both of these methods likely to produce a simple random sample?
        (ii) Which is the best method? Give full reasons for your answers.

7

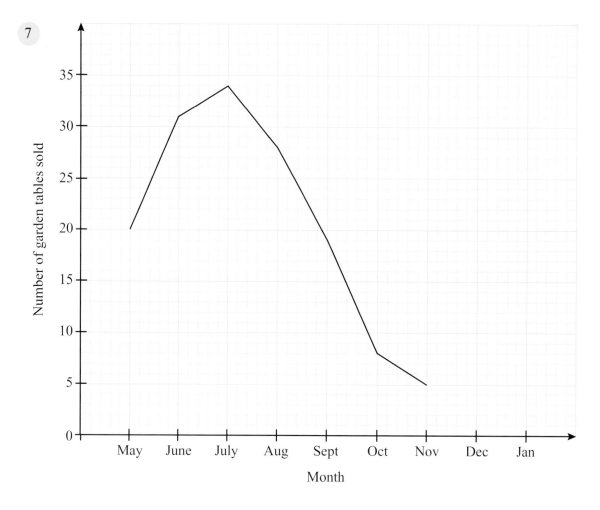

A store sells garden tables. The number sold for some months of the year is shown above.

Can the number of garden tables sold in January be reliably predicted using the graph above?

Give reasons for your answer and state any assumptions you have made.

8 The ages of footballers in two team squads are shown below.

Forest United	
Age	Frequency
19	2
20	4
21	2
22	7
23	1
24	4

Castle Rangers

```
1 | 7 8
2 | 2 2 2 3 3 4 4 5 6 6 7 7 7 8 8 8 9 9 9 9
3 | 0 1 1
```

Key 2|4 means 24

By calculating the mean and range for each team, compare the ages of the footballers in Forest United with those in Castle Rangers.

Hint:
For Forest United, remember to multiply each age by its frequency before adding them up to find the total of all the footballers' ages.

9 A group of 27 people go to an adventure park.
Their first ride is either on the Turbo Terror, the Curly Whirl or the Splashdown. Half of the 12 women go on the Turbo Terror. 5 men go on the Splashdown.

10 people go on the Curly Whirl of whom $\frac{2}{5}$ are women.

How many people in total go on the Splashdown first?

10 The mean average weight of 40 people in a gym is 65 kg.
One hour later, 25 people with mean weight 68 kg have left the gym but
10 people with mean weight 85 kg have come into the gym.
Work out the mean weight of the 25 people now in the gym.

11 The scatter graph below shows the number of drinks Charlie had on certain
days and the maximum temperature reached.

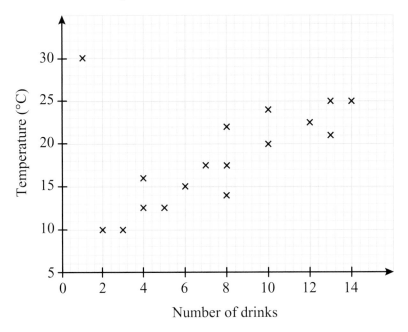

(a) How many drinks would you expect Charlie to have when the maximum
temperature is 21°C?

(b) Write down the values of an outlier.

(c) Why can a line of best fit not be used to estimate the number of drinks
when the maximum temperature is 0°C?

12 There are 400 people on a beach.
The table below shows some
details about these people.

Age	Male	Female
under 21 years	?	?
21–45 years	73	58
over 45 years	69	82

A stratified sample of 40 of these
people is taken.

(a) How many females over 45 years
old would be in the sample?

(b) There are five males under 21 years old in the sample.
Work out the greatest number of the 400 people who might be females
under 21 years old.

M	MIXED 5A

1   Mr Reay is planning a school camp. For safety reasons there must be one teacher for every ten students. 36 students go to the school camp.
The teachers do not pay to go to school camp.

The cost per person of one activity is shown opposite.

If all the students and teachers do one activity, how much will each student need to pay to cover the total cost?

Activity	
Climbing	
Canoeing	£18 per session
Caving	

2   The Highest Common Factor of 80 and 200 is m.
The smallest prime number greater than m is n.
Find the values of two square numbers p and q which add together to equal n.
Show all working out clearly.

3   Callum wants to put some wooden coving in his living room.

The wooden coving is 'shaped' wood which is placed where the wall meets the ceiling. Callum wants the coving to go completely around the living room.

The coving is sold in 4 metre lengths.
The price is shown below as is a plan of Callum's living room.

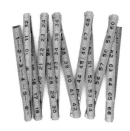

> coving 4 m lengths
> £12.49 each

How much money will Callum need to spend?

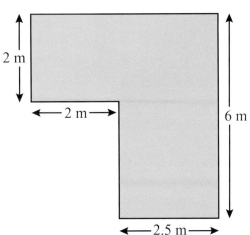

4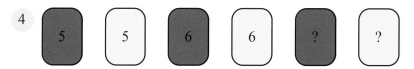

In the list of six numbers above, the mode is 6 and the range is 9.
Calculate the mean for these six numbers.

5 Lucy is asked to factorise $36a^2 - 12ab$ *completely*.
She takes out common factor $4a$ so writes the answer $4a(9a - 3b)$.
Sanjay says that Lucy has not factorised $36a^2 - 12ab$ *completely*.
Explain clearly why Sanjay says this.

6 Bella runs a shop which sells pasties. She records how many steak pasties and
vegetable pasties are sold on each of five days of the week.

This information is shown in the bar chart below.

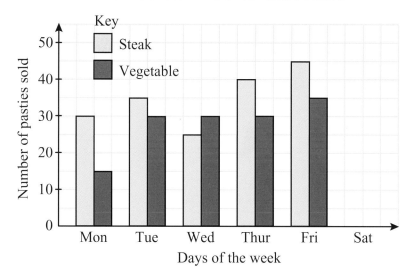

(a) How many vegetable pasties were sold on Friday?

(b) On which day of the week were more vegetable pasties sold than steak pasties?

(c) On Saturday Bella sold 50 steak pasties and 45 vegetable pasties.
Copy then complete the bar chart with this information.

(d) From Monday to Saturday, how many more steak pasties did Bella sell than
vegetable pasties?
Show your working out.

7 Denver buys a caravan for £8000.

Each year it loses 10% of its value at the start of the year.

After two years Denver wants to buy a new caravan for £9000.
How much extra money will he need to find if he sells his old caravan for its value after two years?

8

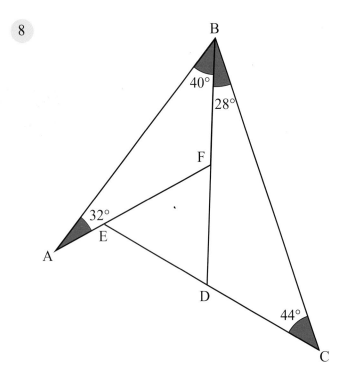

(a) Prove that triangle DEF is isosceles.
You must give full reasons for your answer.

(b) If EF = 5 cm and CD = 3 cm, work out the length CE.

Hint:
Work out angles $A\hat{F}B$ and $B\hat{D}C$ first.

9 The shape opposite consists of a semi-circle and a triangle.
The base of the triangle is 12 cm and its height is 10 cm.
What percentage of the whole shape is yellow?
Give the answer to one decimal place.

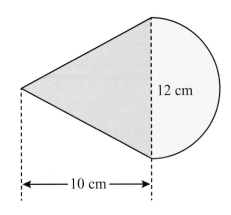

10 80 people are asked if they ate chinese food (C) and indian food (I) during the previous week. The number of people eating each type of food is shown in the Venn diagram below.

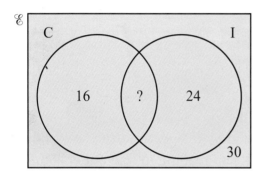

If one person is chosen at random, work out

$$p(C \cap I)$$

11

A snail and a grasshopper race each other 15 times.

The median time for the grasshopper is 17 seconds and the range for its times is 8 seconds.

The snail's times are shown in the stem and leaf diagram below.

```
7 | 2 6 8
8 | 4 7 8 8
9 | 1 3 5 5 7 8 8 9
```

Key 8|7 means 87 seconds

Compare fully the times taken by the snail with the times taken by the grasshopper.

12   Mrs Williams buys her electricity from the Electrogen Company.
Her neighbour, Mr Harris, buys his electricity from the Cotswold Electric
Company. They each receive a quarterly electricity bill as shown below.

Bill for Mrs Williams
Previous reading: 12715   Present reading: 13692   Total: £156.32   VAT (5%): £7.82   Total to pay: £164.14

Bill for Mr Harris
Previous reading: 23187   Present reading: 24312   Total: £168.75   VAT (5%): £8.44   Total to pay: £177.19

Before VAT is added, work out the cost of electricity per unit for each bill.
Which electricity company is cheaper to buy electricity from?

Hint:
Subtract the previous reading from the
present reading to find out how many
units of electricity have been used.

M MIXED 5EXT

1 An electric saw is to be hired for *n* days
to make bird boxes. The cost *C* of hiring
the saw from Hobson's Machinery is
given by the formula $C = 16 + 25n$.
The cost *C* of hiring the saw from
Elliot's Supplies is given by the formula
$C = 48 + 17n$.
The cost *C* is given in pounds.

How many days is the electric saw hired
for if the cost *C* from both shops is the
same amount?

2 Lillian earns £1382.50 each month. Her income tax allowance and the tax rate
are shown below.

Tax allowance per year	£10 600
Tax rate	20%

How much income tax does Lillian have to pay each month?

3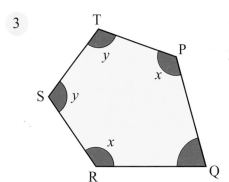

Explain in detail why
$P\widehat{Q}R = 540 - 2x - 2y$
in the pentagon opposite.

4 Prove that

$$2^{-4} = \frac{1}{2^4}$$

> **Hint:**
> Use $a^m \div a^n = a^{m-n}$ and remember $a^0 = 1$

5 Riley travels 14 miles in 15 minutes. She drives at this steady speed for 2 hours from Durham to Sheffield.

The distances from Durham to Sheffield and from Sheffield to London are in the ratio $2:3$.
What is the distance from Sheffield to London?

6 Terry has some car repairs done at his local garage.

He is told how much the bill is and has just enough money to cover it.

Unfortunately the garage quote did not include the VAT.

When Terry gets the actual bill including VAT, it amounts to £270.
Assume VAT is 20%

Calculate how much more money Terry needs to cover this bill than he first thought.

> **Hint:**
> Think about reverse percentages.

7 Alma is asked to find the actual perimeter of the rectangle shown opposite if its area is 18 cm². She does the following working out.

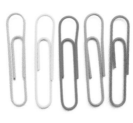

$x + 3$

x

$area = x(x + 3) = 18$

$x^2 + 3x = 18$

$x^2 + 3x - 18 = 0$

$(x - 6)(x + 3) = 0$

$x - 6 = 0 \text{ or } x + 3 = 0$

$x = 6 \text{ or } -3$

A length cannot be negative so $x = 6$ cm

$perimeter = x + x + 3 + x + x + 3$

$= 4x + 6$

$= 24 + 6 \text{ when } x = 6$

$perimeter = 30 \text{ cm}$

Alma is not correct. Explain what mistake she has made.
Show the full correct working out.

8 Lauren has a box of paper clips.
The number of each colour are shown below.

Colour	Frequency
Pink	8
Yellow	2
Green	5
Blue	16
Red	5

Lauren randomly takes three paper clips.
Work out the probability that all three paper clips are the same colour.

Hint:
Consider just P, P, P then Y, Y, Y then G, G, G then B, B, B then R, R, R on a probability tree.

9 The charts below show how many students studied History, Geography and Art
in Lanchester High School in the years shown.

Year 2016

	Male	Female	Total
History	32	40	72
Geography	45	35	80
Art	58	70	128
Total	135	145	280

Work out the percentage increase in the
number of students taking Geography
in 2017 compared to 2016.

Year 2017

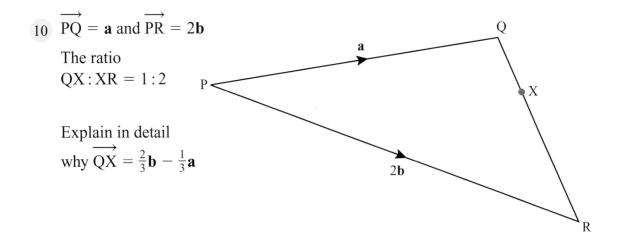

In 2017, there is an increase
of $\frac{1}{7}$ in the total number of
students compared to 2016.

10 $\overrightarrow{PQ} = \mathbf{a}$ and $\overrightarrow{PR} = 2\mathbf{b}$

The ratio
$QX : XR = 1 : 2$

Explain in detail
why $\overrightarrow{QX} = \frac{2}{3}\mathbf{b} - \frac{1}{3}\mathbf{a}$

11 The hemisphere opposite has diameter 18 cm.
Ian and Asha have no calculator.
Ian says that the total surface area of
the hemisphere is 162π cm².
Asha says that the total surface area of
the hemisphere is 243π cm².
Explain in detail who is correct.

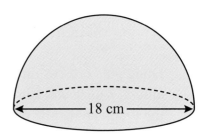

18 cm

Hint:
surface area of a sphere = $4\pi r^2$

12

B

$x + 40$

$2x$ $2y$

A   C

Q

$x + 55$

$3y - 35$ $x + 25$

P   R

Work out the actual values of each angle in the two triangles above.

Hint:
Form simultaneous equations
then solve them.

G GEOMETRY 3A

1 Doug puts crosses on a graph at (2, 0), (0, 2) and (2, 4). He wants to put another cross on the graph so that he can join up all the crosses to make a square.
Chen says he should put a final cross at (4, 3).
Is Chen correct? You must justify your answer fully.

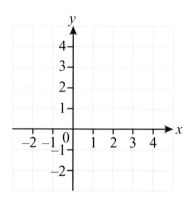

2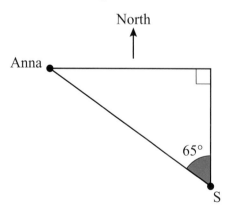

The plan of a building is shown opposite. The side AB is 18 m in real life.
Explain clearly why the scale of the map is 1 : 300.

A ◀— 6 cm —▶ B

3 The diagram below shows Anna's position near the start of a bridge S.

North

Anna

65°

S

Work out the bearing of S from Anna.

Hint:
A bearing is measured *clockwise* from the North line.

4 Mark uses cubes to make the object below.

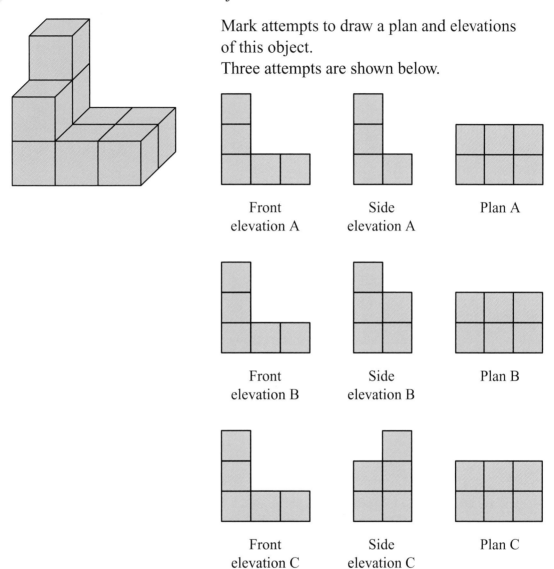

Mark attempts to draw a plan and elevations of this object.
Three attempts are shown below.

Front elevation A   Side elevation A   Plan A

Front elevation B   Side elevation B   Plan B

Front elevation C   Side elevation C   Plan C

Has Mark drawn one correct plan and elevations?
Write down A, B or C if one of these is correct or draw the correct plan and elevations.

5 The net opposite is folded
   together to make a prism.

   How many edges does the
   prism have?

   (All lengths are in cm.)

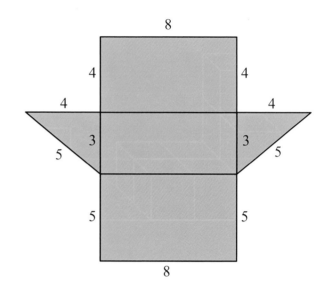

6

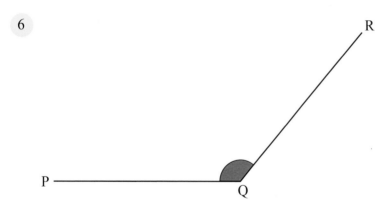

Mariana uses a
protractor to measure
P$\widehat{Q}$R opposite.

She writes down the
answer 230°.

What mistake has
Mariana made and why
do you think she made
this mistake?

7 Two maps show the same section
   of the Great Wall of China.
   This section is 2 cm long on one
   of the maps with scale 1 : 20000.
   How many millimetres long is
   this same section on the other
   map which has scale 1 : 50000?

8 A ship is sailing on a bearing of 043°.
It now needs to sail South West.
The ship can turn clockwise or anti-clockwise.

(a) If the ship is to turn by the least angle, should it turn clockwise or
anti-clockwise?

(b) Write down the least angle that the ship needs to turn.

9 Kabir is asked to construct the triangle
shown opposite by using a ruler and
protractor only.
Explain clearly why this is impossible.

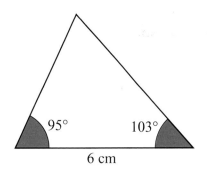

95°   103°

6 cm

10

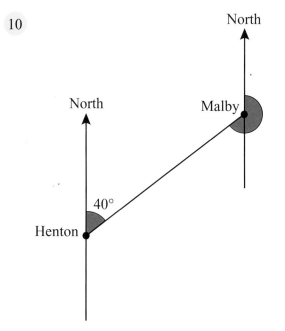

North

North

Malby

40°

Henton

The bearing of Malby from Henton
is 040°.
Work out the bearing of Henton from
Malby as shown.

11 Five points on a graph have the following co-ordinates:
A(5, 4), B(3, 0), C(1, −2), D(−3, 0) and E(1, 4).
Crosses are drawn at the midpoints of lines AB, BC, CD and DE.
These crosses are then joined
together with straight lines to
make a quadrilateral.
Name the quadrilateral.

Hint:
Draw axes and plot the
points A to E first.

12

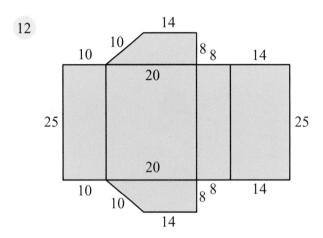

The net of a prism is shown
opposite.
All lengths are in cm.
Work out the volume of this
prism.

Hint:
volume of prism = cross-
sectional area × length

G | GEOMETRY 3EXT

1

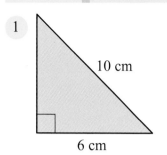

10 cm

6 cm

Calculate the area of this triangle.

> **Hint:**
> Use Pythagoras first.

2

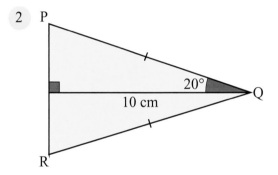

P

20°

10 cm

Q

R

Triangle PQR is isosceles.
Calculate the perimeter of triangle PQR, giving your answer to one decimal place.

> **Hint:**
> Remember SOHCAHTOA

3

A window cleaner leans a ladder against a wall.

The bottom of the ladder is 1.65 m from the wall.

The top of the ladder reaches up to the bottom of a window which is 3.96 m above the ground.

Work out the length of the ladder.

4 The plan and elevations of a house are shown below.

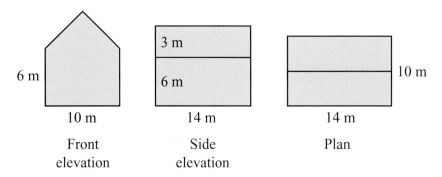

Calculate the volume of the house.

5

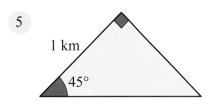

Harley runs twice around the triangular track shown opposite at a constant speed of 4 m/s.

How long does this take Harley to complete?

Give the answer in minutes to 3 significant figures.

Hint:

$\tan 45° = 1$ and $\cos 45° = \dfrac{\sqrt{2}}{2}$

6

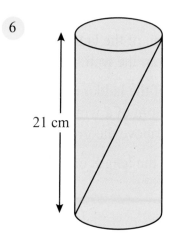

A pencil case is in the shape of a cylinder.

Its length is 21 cm and its radius is 5 cm.

Can a pencil of length 23 cm fit inside this pencil case?

You must show all your working out.

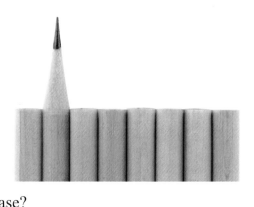

7

Jason walks 250 m south from some pyramids then 400 m east.

On what bearing must he now walk if he wants to return directly to the pyramids?

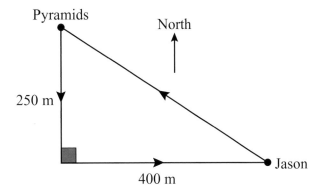

8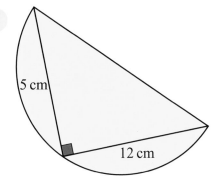

Calculate the perimeter of this semi-circle.

Give your answer to one decimal place.

9 The diagram opposite shows the side of a house AB and a square garden with side length 10 m. The owner wants to build a patio which is up to 5 m from the side of the house and at least 5 m from corner A. Draw the diagram using a scale of 1 cm to 1 m then show exactly where the patio is placed.

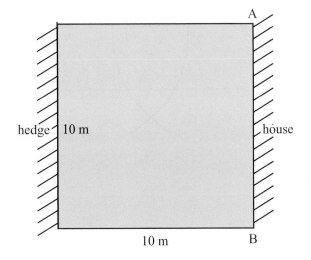

10

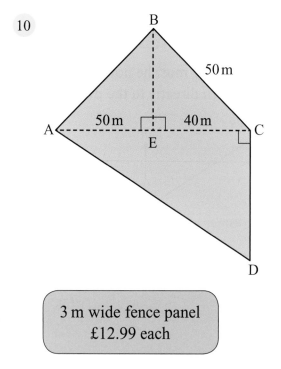

A farmer wants to put fencing completely around the field shown opposite.
The length CD is equal to the length AC.

Each outer edge of the field will be fenced using 3 m wide fence panels. Parts of a fence panel cannot be used on more than one side of the field.

What is the least amount the farmer will have to pay for all the fence panels?

3 m wide fence panel
£12.99 each

11

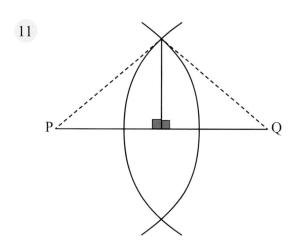

Evie has used compasses and ruler only to construct the perpendicular bisector of line PQ.

Explain fully why the perpendicular bisector construction method works.

Hint:
Consider the diagonals of a rhombus.

12

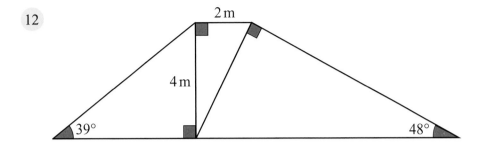

The steel framework for part of a roof is shown above. Each side of each triangle is a steel girder.

Calculate the total length of steel that is required for this framework.

Give your answer to one decimal place.

M | MIXED 6A

1 Colin and eleven of his friends plan to have a game of golf then a set meal.
The prices are shown below:

Golf
£28 per person
15% off for groups
of 10 or more

Set meal
£15 per person
or £35 for every
3 people

Colin has £440 to pay for all the golf and the meals.
The money left over is to be given as a tip.
Work out how much the tip will be.

2 Ella wants to buy 3 kg of cherries.
The local shop sells cherries in 3
different sizes.

£2.20
1 kg

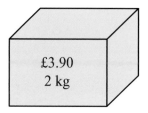

£3.90
2 kg

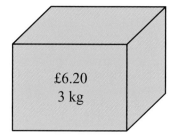

£6.20
3 kg

What is the cheapest way of Ella buying 3 kg of cherries?
Show all your working out.

3 The table below shows how many main meals were sold during one week in two Indian restaurants.

	Mon.	Tues.	Wed.	Thurs.	Fri.	Sat.	Sun.
The Rajah	10	14	26	30	58	60	28
Spice House	22	28	30	28	32	36	20

Claire wants to compare the number of main meals sold in The Rajah with the number of main meals sold in the Spice House.

On squared paper, draw a suitable chart or diagram she could use.

4

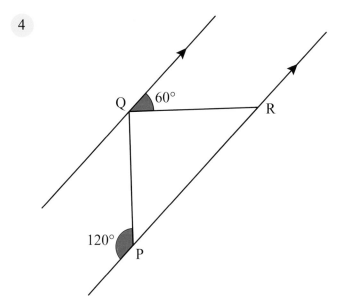

Explain in detail why triangle PQR is equilateral.

5 In a Sports Club at 6 p.m. last Tuesday there were 63 people either in the gym, playing badminton or boxing.

A quarter of the 28 men were boxing. Half of the 20 people playing badminton were women. There were 20 women in the gym.

Find the total number of people who were boxing.

6   Kevin has 13 innings in cricket and makes the scores shown below.

      8 82 17 51 39 6 12 42 37 68 19 46 58

(a) Find his median score.

(b) Find the range of his scores.

(c) James has 17 innings. His scores are shown in the stem and leaf diagram below.

    1 | 9
    2 | 1 3 3
    3 | 2 5
    4 | 6
    5 | 4 7 7 9
    6 | 1 2 2 5 8
    7 | 2

> Key 4|6 means 46 runs

Use the median and range to compare the scores for Kevin with the scores for James.

7   $3(2x + 5) + 5(2x + 9) = a(4x + 15)$

Work out the value of a.

Show all your working out clearly.

8   Edward plans to wallpaper two complete walls in his living room. Each wall is 2.5 m high and a plan of the living room is shown opposite.

A wallpaper roll is 8 m long and 80 cm wide.

Each roll of wallpaper costs £18.50

How many rolls of wallpaper will Edward need and what will be the total cost?

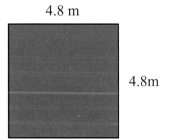

4.8 m

4.8m

9　Bryan lives in Wells. He wants to meet a friend in Bath for a pizza.
He needs to travel by bus. The bus timetable is shown below.

173: Wells – Bath										
Service No.:	173	173	173	173	173	173	173	173	173	173
Wells Bus Station	0655	0750	0943	1043	1143	1243	1343	1443	1543	1643
Gurney Slade	0715	0810	1003	1103	1203	1303	1403	1503	1603	1703
Chilcompton	0721	0816	1009	1109	1209	1309	1409	1509	1609	1709
Radstock	0743	0839	1031	1131	1231	1331	1431	1531	1631	1731
Dunkerton	0756	0853	1044	1144	1244	1344	1444	1544	1644	1744
Bath, Bus Station	0812	0909	1100	1200	1300	1400	1500	1600	1700	1800
173: Bath – Wells										
Bath, Bus Station	– – –	0910	1010	1110	1210	1310	1410	1510	1610	1710
Dunkerton	– – –	0924	1024	1124	1224	1324	1424	1524	1624	1724
Radstock	– – –	0940	1040	1140	1240	1340	1440	1540	1640	1740
Chilcompton	0756	0957	1057	1157	1257	1357	1457	1557	1657	1757
Gurney Slade	0806	1007	1107	1207	1307	1407	1507	1607	1707	1807
Wells Bus Station	0826	1027	1127	1227	1327	1427	1527	1627	1727	1827

It takes Bryan 20 minutes to walk from his home to Wells Bus Station.

It takes him 15 minutes to walk from Bath Bus Station to the pizza restaurant.
He has arranged to meet his friend at Bath Bus Station at 1:10 pm.

They spend $1\frac{1}{2}$ hours at the pizza restaurant. Bryan then heads straight back to
the bus station and catches the first possible bus home. He then walks directly
back to his house.

At what time should Bryan arrive back home?

10 Kylie is designing a paper weight as shown below. Blue objects A and B are made from the same material and must weigh the same amount. What length x should object B be made by Kylie?

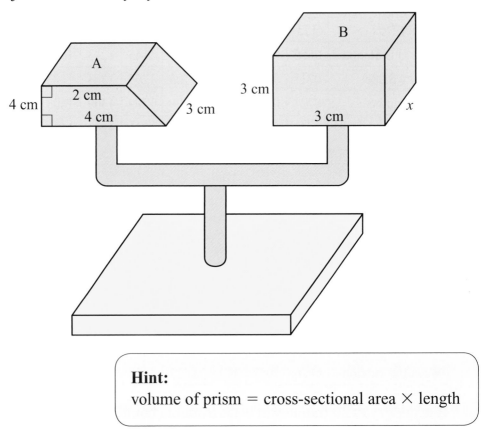

> **Hint:**
> volume of prism = cross-sectional area × length

11 Cole owns an i-phone. He pays a monthly contract of £35 as set out below:

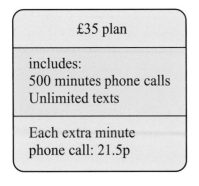

£35 plan
includes: 500 minutes phone calls Unlimited texts
Each extra minute phone call: 21.5p

In April, Cole makes 628 minutes of phone calls and 802 texts. How much does Cole have to pay for his i-phone at the end of April?

12 In the diagram opposite, B is on a
bearing of 040° from A.
AC runs from West to East.
Work out the bearing of B from C.

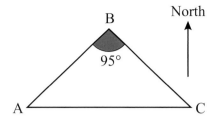

Hint:
The bearing of P from Q is the angle
measured clockwise from the North
line at Q.

1   Blake and Maya help Lauren to decorate a room for her grandmother.
They are paid a total of £792 for doing the job. Blake receives $\frac{1}{6}$ of the money.

The rest of the money is split in the ratio 4 : 7 between Maya and Lauren.
How much more money does Maya get than Blake?

2   45 married people are asked where they
got married.
The information is shown in the table below.

Place	Frequency
Registry office	16
In another country	4
Church	20
Other places	5

Represent this information in a suitable diagram
or chart.

3   In a supermarket, 'CLEANSE' dishwasher tablets are sold in three sizes of box
as shown below:

CLEANSE
56
tablets

£12.15

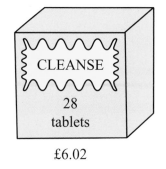

CLEANSE
28
tablets

£6.02

CLEANSE
14
tablets

£3.28

Which box is the best value for money? Show all your working out.

4 A box contains red, blue and green balls. If one ball is removed at random, the probability of choosing each colour is shown below.

red	blue	green
0.01	0.5	0.49

(a) Explain clearly why there must be at least 100 balls in the box.

(b) How many balls in the box are green if there are 300 balls in total?

5 (a) Express 0.1 as a fraction.

(b) Use diagrams to explain clearly why
   $6 \div 0.1 = 60$

(c) Explain clearly why $6 \div 0.2 = 30$

6

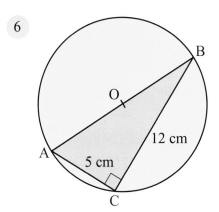

What percentage of this circle is yellow if AB is the diameter of the circle and AB = 13 cm?
Give the answer to one decimal place.

Hint:
To work out a as a percentage of b, calculate $\dfrac{a}{b} \times 100\%$

7 Julie lives in Peckford. She wants to spend two hours ice skating in Tenby and at least one-and-a-half hours having a meal and drink afterwards. A bus timetable from Hatton to Tenby is shown below.

Hatton	0950	1030	1130	1230	1330	1430	1450	1530	1550
Marby	1013	1053	1153	1253	1353	1453	1513	1553	1613
Peckford	1025	1105	1205	1305	1405	1505	1525	1605	1625
Neane	1047	1127	1227	1327	1427	1527	1547	1627	1647
Tenby	1105	1145	1245	1345	1445	1545	1605	1645	1705

A bus timetable from Tenby to Hatton is shown below.

Tenby	1535	1635	1735	1835	1935	2035	2135	2235	2305
Neane	1554	1654	1754	1854	1954	2054	2154	2254	2324
Peckford	1616	1716	1816	1916	2016	2116	2216	2316	2346
Marby	1628	1728	1828	1928	2028	2128	2228	2328	2358
Hatton	1650	1750	1850	1950	2050	2150	2250	2350	0020

Tenby ice skating sessions		
	Open	
1100	to	1330
1430	to	1700
1800	to	2030

Julie takes 10 minutes to walk from her home to the Peckford bus stop.

She takes 25 minutes to walk from Tenby Bus Station to the ice skating centre.

The table opposite shows when ice skating is possible.

If Julie leaves her home at 1245, what is the earliest bus she might want to catch *home from Tenby*?

If she catches this bus, what time should she arrive home?

Show all your working out fully.

8 A triangle P is reflected in the *y*-axis then its image (the new triangle) is reflected in the *x*-axis. The final triangle is named Q.
Describe the single transformation that will transform triangle P directly to triangle Q.

> **Hint:**
> Draw axes and a triangle then do the given transformations.

9 Mrs Parker wants three sides of her house to be painted. Painter, Carl, offers to do the whole job for £450. Another painter, Helen, offers to do the job for £3 per square metre.

The three sides of the house to be painted are shown below.
Each window has area 2 m².
Each door has area 2.5 m².

Who should Mrs Parker choose to paint her house so that she spends the least amount of money?
How much cheaper is this painter?

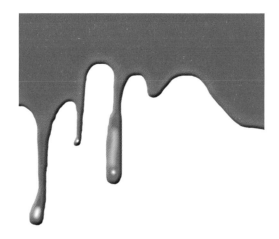

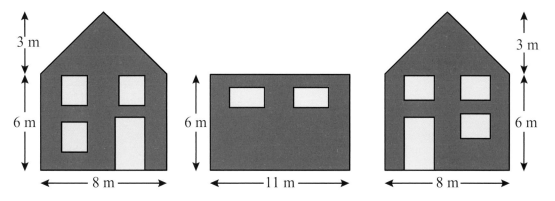

3 m   6 m   8 m

6 m   11 m

3 m   6 m   8 m

10 The nth term of sequence A is $7n + 2$.
Another sequence B starts with 3, 9, 15, 21, …
Liv says that the 8th term of sequence B has the same value as the 7th term of sequence A.
Show clearly whether Liv is correct or not.

11 Candice is researching how often people take the bus. She asks 40 people in a city and 40 people in a village how often they took a bus in the last week.
The table below shows the results for the city.

City	
Number of bus trips	Frequency
0	12
1	3
2	2
3	1
4	3
5	0
6	1
7	0
8	3
9	0
10	15

The village mean and range is shown below.

Village
Mean = 1.3 bus trips
Range = 10 bus trips

Compare fully the number of bus trips taken by people in the city with the number of bus trips taken by people in the village.

12 27 students from a Music College
go for a drink.
Their main instruments are
either piano, violin or cello.

9 of the 15 women play the
violin.

$\frac{2}{3}$ of the six piano players are
men.

6 men play the cello.

How many students in total
play the violin?

M	**MIXED 6C**

1   Wyatt has four cards each with a number on it.

| 1 | | 2 | | 7 | | ? |

If the median of these four numbers is 2, what is the mean average for these four numbers?

2   Each white circle in this photo has radius 5 cm.
The whole shape is a rectangle of length 1 metre
and width 68 cm.

Calculate the black area.
Give the answer to the nearest whole number in cm^2.

3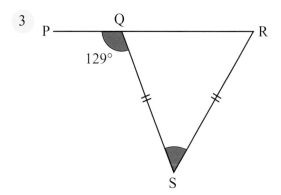

Triangle QRS is isosceles.

Work out the size of angle QSR.

You must give reasons for each step in your working.

4

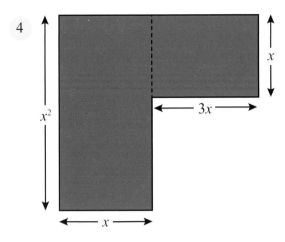

(a) Write down an expression, in terms of x, for the total area of this L-shape.

(b) Calculate the actual area of this L-shape when $x = 4$ cm.

5 Paige usually drives to work in 20 minutes at a steady speed of 45 mph. She always arrives at work at 9 am.
One morning Paige comes out of her house at 8:40 am but takes 5 minutes to clear some snow off her car.
At what speed must she now drive to still get to work at 9 am?

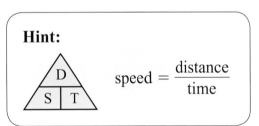

Hint:

$$\text{speed} = \frac{\text{distance}}{\text{time}}$$

6

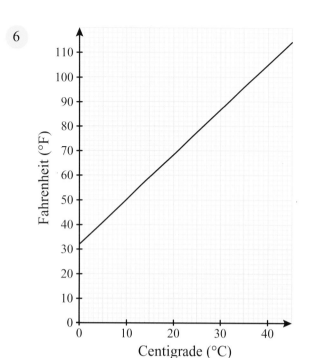

This graph can be used to convert degrees Fahrenheit into degrees Centigrade and vice versa.

Eric looks at five possible holiday destinations. He will not go to a place where the maximum temperature might go above 90 °F.

Write down which of the five places, in the table below, he will not go to on holiday.

Place	Maximum temperature
Barcelona	36 °C
Lisbon	31 °C
Nice	34 °C
Venice	35 °C
Belgrade	30 °C

7

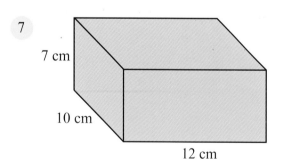

7 cm
10 cm
12 cm

Parker covers this box with wrapping paper. He uses an extra 90 cm² of wrapping paper for overlaps.

What area of wrapping paper will he have left from a square sheet measuring 50 cm × 50 cm?

8 The Venn diagram below shows some letters in the alphabet.

P = {vowels} and Q = {letters in the second half of the alphabet}.

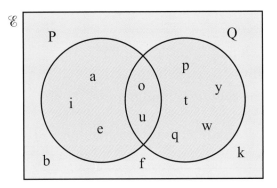

Work out

(a) $n(P \cap Q)$

(b) $p(P')$

Hint:
Each member of a set is called an element.
$n(A)$ means 'the number of elements in set A'
A ∩ B means 'A intersection B'
(elements in both A and B)
A' is 'the complement of A'
(everything not in A)

9 Henry records the types of motorbike he sees at a motorbike show. He sees 90 in total. The findings are shown in the table below.

Type	Frequency
Kawasaki	16
Yamaha	8
Harley Davidson	14
Ducati	12
Honda	?
Suzuki	20

Represent this information in a suitable diagram or chart.

10 The table opposite shows the price of an XIV dishwasher at the end of each year shown.

Cameron buys an XIV dishwasher at the end of 2008.

He pays £4.54 each month insurance for repairs to his dishwasher or help towards buying a new dishwasher.

Year	Price
2007	£742
2008	£762
2009	£787
2010	£814
2011	£838

During	Percentage of new dishwasher
Year 1	100%
Year 2	80%
Year 3	60%
Year 4	40%
Year 5	20%

If his dishwasher cannot be mended, the insurance will pay a percentage of the cost of a new dishwasher as shown in the table opposite.

Cameron's dishwasher breaks down at the end of 2011.
He has to buy a new XIV dishwasher.

(a) How much money for the new dishwasher is paid from the insurance?

(b) Has Cameron saved money overall by making monthly insurance payments? If so, how much money has he saved?

11 (a) Copy the axes shown opposite.

(b) Plot the points A(−1, 2), B(6, 2), C(4, −2) and D(−3, −2) then join them to make a parallelogram.

(c) On the same axes draw any rectangle which has the same area as parallelogram ABCD. Write down the length and width of this rectangle.

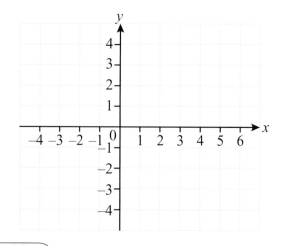

Hint:
area of parallelogram = base × height

12   Ten friends plan a day trip to the seaside. They can get there by minibus taxi or by train. The prices are shown below:

Train	£15.60 day return

Minibus taxi for 10 people
£103.50

Each friend has a train railcard which gives each one of them a 30% discount.

(a) The minibus appears to be cheaper.
How much will each friend save compared to using the train?

(b) On the day, one friend is ill. The other 9 friends still have to use the taxi.
This is now more expensive for each of them than using the train.
By how much?

1   Luka is fixing tiles onto the walls in his bathroom.
    He uses 7 blue tiles for every 4 white tiles.
    He uses two sizes of white tiles, large and small, in the ratio 1 : 5.
    Luka uses a total of 210 blue tiles.
    How many small white tiles does he use?

2   A certain make of car costs £11 500 when it was brand new.
    The values of some cars of this make are recorded in the years that follow.
    The values are shown on the scatter graph below.

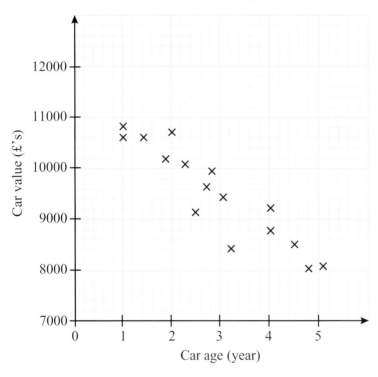

    (a) Describe the relationship between the car value and the car age.
    (b) Copy the scatter graph then estimate the
        value of a car which is 3.5 years old.
    (c) Why can the value of a 9 year old car not be
        reliably estimated from the above data?

    Hint:
    Draw a line of best fit.

3　Find the value of the length x if the triangle and the rectangle both have the same area.

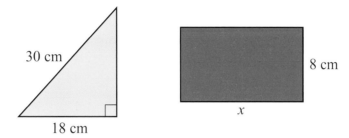

4　Tara simplifies an expression as shown below.

$$(x + 4)^2 + 6(2x + 1)$$
$$= x^2 + 16 + 12x + 1$$
$$= x^2 + 12x + 17$$

Explain very carefully each mistake that Tara has made.
What should the final answer be?

5　

A fire service helicopter is 8 km south and 3 km east of a fire.

How far and on what bearing must the helicopter fly to directly reach the fire? Give both answers to one decimal place.

> **Hint:**
> Draw a diagram and use trigonometry.

6

P, Q, R, S, T rectangle with triangle, angle x marked at P.

PQST is a rectangle.

PRT is an isosceles triangle.

Express angle PRT in terms of x.

Explain your reasons fully.

Hint:
$T\hat{P}R = 90 - x$

7 Denton brings some bottles of wine back from France in his van.
He gives 80% of the wine to a friend.

His brother, sister and father receive the remaining wine in the ratio $2 : 1 : 5$.

Denton bought all the wine in boxes of twelve. If he gave his father 45 bottles of wine, how many boxes did Denton bring back from France?

Hint:
This question involves reverse percentages.

8

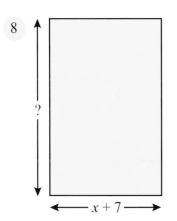

The area of this rectangle is given by the expression $(x^2 + 16x + 63)\,\text{cm}^2$

The width is $(x + 7)\,\text{cm}$ as shown.

Find an expression for the perimeter of the rectangle.

9 There are some yellow and black beads in a bag.
One bead is removed from the bag then replaced. Another bead is then removed.
The probability of removing two black beads is $\frac{16}{49}$.
What originally was the probability of removing one yellow bead?

> **Hint:**
> Think about the use of a probability tree.

10 A dancing competition is taking place.
Dom and Elena have scored 26 points
more than Brody and Grace.
Dom and Elena have scored three
times more points than Max and
Asha. Henry and Brooke have scored
10 points less than Max and Asha.
They have all scored 524 points in
total. How many points have Dom
and Elena scored?

> **Hint:**
> Let one of the players' scores
> equal n then make an equation.

11 Ashna invests £4000 at 3% compound
interest per annum.
Julian invests £3500 at 5% compound
interest per annum.
During which year will Julian first have
more money than Ashna?
Explain your method fully.

> **Hint:**
> Use the multipliers,
> e.g. $\times 1.02$ for 2%
> compound interest per
> annum.

12

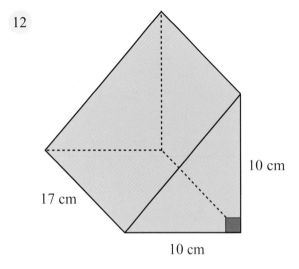

17 cm

10 cm

10 cm

Aaron has a 2 m by 40 cm rectangular sheet of wrapping paper.

He wraps the box shown opposite which is in the shape of a triangular prism.

He uses 40% more wrapping paper than the actual surface area of the box.

Calculate the percentage of the original rectangular sheet of wrapping paper which is used by Aaron to wrap this box.

Give the answer to one decimal place.

Hint:
Remember to use Pythagoras.

ANSWERS

PART ONE

Number 1A   Page 1

(ref. Foundation GCSE Maths 1–3 & 4–5 Unit 1)

1   Multiply before add. Answer should be 13.

2   (a) No   (b) Kate needs to save another £49

3   13:50

4   63 500

5   Morley rugby club by £1300

6   14°C or −18°C

7   (a) Does not matter.   (b) $2 \times 2 \times 3 \times 5$

8   300 miles

9   August 12th

10   5 months

11   −8

12   (a) No, they would need at least £10.20
     (b) £3.60

Number 1B   Page 5

(ref. Foundation GCSE Maths 1–3 & 4–5 Unit 1)

1   e.g. $m = 5, n = 2, p = 11$

2   Louise by £90

3   (a) 12 by 12   (b) 24 by 6

4   4

5   11:30 p.m.

6   1616

7   (a) 64   (b) Use brackets $(-8)^2$

8   £54.15

9   £152

10   (a) 28 incorrect and 4 at the bottom is not prime
     (c) $96 = 2 \times 2 \times 2 \times 2 \times 2 \times 3$

11   Food is OK. −1°C at 5 a.m. so by 7 a.m. the temperature has not been above 0°C for 2 hours.

12   £327

Number 1EXT   Page 8

(ref. Foundation GCSE Maths 1–3 & 4–5 Unit 1)

1   (a) Counted three 0's as the number for the power of 10
     (b) 6.25×10^5

2   231 km

3   4000

4   £97

5   (a) £12.50
     (b) No. Another £100 is needed.

6   2520

7   £230

8   £22.52

9   36 120 000 computers

10   $\frac{1}{64}$

11   $A = 252, B = 700$

12   skis from shop B, jackets from shop C and ski passes from shop A. Total €914

Algebra 1A   Page 13

(ref. Foundation GCSE Maths 1–3 & 4–5 Unit 2)

1   $4x + 3y - 1$

2   (a) should work out a^2 first   (b) 12

3   shape P: $12x + 6$, shape Q: $12x + 4$, shape R: $12x + 5$ hence shape P has the largest perimeter

4   Q

5   both are n^5

6   (a) $42x$ (b) $3x$

7   (a) $15 \div 6$ would equal 2.5   (b) 54

8   $6a + 9b$

9   (a) $4(7x + 2) = 28x + 8$ (b) 176

10   (a) Eva
     (b) she should also have taken out the common factor 2.

11 20

12 $4n + 2$

Algebra 1EXT Page 16
(ref. Foundation GCSE Maths 1–3 & 4–5 Unit 2)

1 (a) $14x + 8 = 36$ (b) $x = 2$ (c) $65\,\text{m}^2$

2 (a) should have added 4 to both sides
   (b) 5

3 15

4 £75

5 $n^2 + 7n + 12$

6 (a) No, not ready until $1{:}02\frac{1}{2}$ p.m.
   (b) 3 kg

7 2

8 no mistakes made

9 15 cm

10 17

11 $n - 2$

12 44 cm

Mixed 1A Page 20
(ref. Foundation GCSE Maths 1–3 & 4–5 Units 1, 2)

1 Emma correct

2 £78.75

3 July

4 both sides equal $6n + 15$

5 £44.46

6 flat B cheaper by £4.20 per week

7 (a) P greater ($= 27$ compared to 0 and 13)
   (b) Q greater ($= 0$ compared to -9 and -17)

8 8 pieces (six for 2×1.2 m and 1×1 m,
   two for 3×1 m) or (four for 2×1.2 m and
   1×1 m, four for 1×1.2 m and 2×1 m)

9 4

10 36°

11 969

12 £2.97

Mixed 1B Page 24
(ref. Foundation GCSE Maths 1–3 & 4–5 Units 1, 2)

1 9 cm

2 (a) $n^2 \times n^2 \times n^2$ (b) $3n^2$

3 (a) $2x + 6y$
   (b) $5y$
   (c) e.g. large 25, small 10, lots of possibilities

4 not correct. It should be $3 \times (6 - 2) + 4$

5 9

6 doubling a whole number means the answer must
   be a multiple of 2, i.e. even

7 Carmark cheaper by £42

8 (a) $26n + 2$ (b) $2(13n + 1)$

9 18 minutes

10 £130

11 (a) $8x - 28$ (b) $8x^2 - 28x$ (c) $2x^4 - 7x^2$

12 Friday: five 8 packs for £11.75
    Saturday: three 8 packs, one 4 pack, one 2 pack
    for £8.91

Mixed 1EXT Page 28
(ref. Foundation GCSE Maths 1–3 & 4–5 Units 1, 2)

1 $96\,\text{cm}^2$

2 false. $x^2 - 6x + 8 = (x - 2)(x - 4)$

3 (a) $\frac{1}{48}$ (b) $\frac{1}{48}$ (c) the same

4 4.2 (light) years

5 0 bread rolls and 4 packets of crisps

6 (a) Olivia
   (b) Hayden should have multiplied 5 by 4
   (c) try the number in the given equation to see if
       it works

7 $x = 30°$, angles are 60°, 70°, 50°

8 1×10^{-2}

9 $351\,\text{cm}^2$

10 Polly is correct

11 Yes, she raises £107.10

12 $\frac{1}{12}$

Number 2A   Page 32

(ref. Foundation GCSE Maths 1–3 & 4–5 Unit 3)

1 (a) 3   (b) 24   (c) 24   (d) 36

2 29

3 Yes, 64 cm of ribbon remains

4 Correct. $\frac{3}{5} = \frac{6}{10}$ and $0.4 = \frac{4}{10}$

5 Yes the target is met. $\frac{3}{4}$ sales $>$ target $\frac{2}{3}$ sales.

6 Show $\frac{4}{12} + \frac{3}{12} = \frac{7}{12}$

7 20

8 $\frac{5}{24}$

9 12

10 Correct. e.g. add zeros to some numbers so all the numbers have the same number of digits after the decimal point then it is easier to compare the numbers.

11 21

12 Yes. Overflow capacity 22 000
      Number of people 21 768

Number 2EXT   Page 36

(ref. Foundation GCSE Maths 1–3 & 4–5 Unit 3)

1 Should be $\frac{6}{15} + \frac{5}{15} = \frac{11}{15}$

2 $\frac{11}{20}$

3 No, it will take until 10:15

4 $\frac{11}{15}$

5 (a) There are four quarters in each whole unit so 4×9 in 9 whole units
    (b) 12

6 $\frac{3}{5}$

7 £42

8 $\frac{31}{80}$

9 5 boxes

10 $\frac{47}{56}$

11 $\frac{n + m}{mn}$

12 Needs 11 cans so £6.10 (6 cans, 3 cans and two $\times$ 1 can)

Mixed 2A   Page 40

(ref. Foundation GCSE Maths 1–3 & 4–5 Units 1, 2, 3)

1 He is correct.

2 £3.60

3 $a^2 + b$ gives the same answer as $a - 2b$ (both $= 5$). $3(2a - b) = -6$

4 48

5 $476

6 Any two numbers from 108, 144, 180

7 $\frac{4}{5}\left(= \frac{28}{35}\right)$ is larger than $\frac{5}{7}\left(= \frac{25}{35}\right)$

8 $a = 7, b = 6$

9 £90.20

10 11, 17 and 19

11 (a) $(2^4)^2 = 2^8$ not 2^6 (b) 2^6

12 £23.35 profit

Mixed 2EXT   Page 44

(ref. Foundation GCSE Maths 1–3 & 4–5 Units 1, 2, 3)

1 False. Should be $8\frac{1}{15}$

2 $x = 4$

3 (a) 4, 9, 49
    (b) maybe examined square numbers

4 195 cm

5 (a) 10   (c) 100

6 (a) Melanie earns £20 more
    (b) No. Robert earns £105 more

7 $\frac{1}{64}$

8 $A = 70, B = 126$

9 $1\frac{17}{30}$ miles

10 6:20 a.m. Manchester to Cairo
     1:05 p.m. Cairo to Manchester
     14 nights in 3* hotel
     Total cost: £1399

11 She is correct.

12 £15 683

Geometry 1A   Page 49

(ref. Foundation GCSE Maths 1–3 & 4–5 Unit 4)

1   54°

3   $B\hat{C}D = 114°$, $Q\hat{R}S = 123°$

4   (a) W   (b) M

5   150°

6   93°

7   35°

8   $\left(3\frac{1}{2}, 3\right)$

9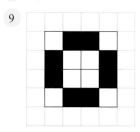

10   12°

11   (a) 65°   (b) not parallel

12   60°

Geometry 1B   Page 54

(ref. Foundation GCSE Maths 1–3 & 4–5 Unit 4)

1   $a = -5, b = 3$

2   81°

3   44°

5   115°

6   75°

7   56°

8   54 cm

9   65°

10   20°

11   1260°

12   Any suitable design containing the enlargements of shape P.

Geometry 1EXT   Page 58

(ref. Foundation GCSE Maths 1–3 & 4–5 Unit 4)

1   115°

2   $\begin{pmatrix} 2 \\ -5 \end{pmatrix}$

3   37°

4   (a) (5, 2)

(b) (5, 2)

(c) The same, so point D is in the same position.

5   70°, 70° or 40°, 100°

6   55°

7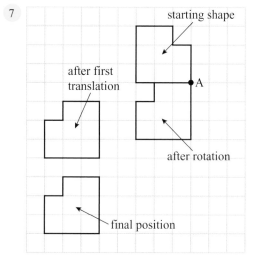

8   $\overrightarrow{AB} = \begin{pmatrix} 3 \\ 2 \end{pmatrix}$, $\overrightarrow{BC} = \begin{pmatrix} 4 \\ 3 \end{pmatrix}$ and $\overrightarrow{AC} = \begin{pmatrix} 7 \\ 5 \end{pmatrix}$

so $\overrightarrow{AB} + \overrightarrow{BC} = \overrightarrow{AC}$

9   144°

10   (c) (−4, 4)

12   $y = 160 - x$

Number 3A   Page 63

(ref. Foundation GCSE Maths 1–3 & 4–5 Unit 5)

1   7:5

2   £2.84

3   30p less

4   £126.36

6   £164.80, £15.80, £33, £82.40, VAT = £59.20, total cost = £355.20

7   London. An extra 8.46 euros.

8   No, she would need another £26

9   wash including 4 wheel scrub (from £5.20 after petrol is paid).

10 (a) £159.50, £15.70, £175.20, £35.04, £210.24
    (b) monthly instalment = £70.08

11 £180

12 Cresswall Cinema by taxi (£15.40 per person) (Cresswall by bus £15.50 pp, Albert by taxi £15.60 pp)

Number 3B   Page 67

(ref. Foundation GCSE Maths 1–3 & 4–5 Unit 5)

1   $\frac{4}{5} = \frac{8}{10} = 0.8$

2   £34, £47.55, £27.20, £209.20, £41.84, £251.04

3   15:13

4   Techshow £208

5   £64.40

6   £7256.40

7   £130

8   1500 euros

9   Deal 3 (£378) better than Deal 1 (£390) and Deal 2 (£425)

10 Both pay £288

11 68

12 Plan A: £162   Plan B: £172   Plan A is cheaper

Number 3C   Page 71

(ref. Foundation GCSE Maths 1–3 & 4–5 Unit 5)

1   below by £24.64

2   Mary correct with 0.0308 (zeros are counted after the first non-zero digit is counted)

3   Matsons (£168) better than other prices £174 and £180

4   2 km : 1200 m = 5 : 3

5   Yes with 9 pence left over

6   Belgium

7   contains exactly 450 ml of water

8   $\frac{3}{10} \times \frac{24}{100} = \frac{72}{1000} = 0.072$

9   330

10 VAT for chairs should be £4.80. Total to pay should be £110.40

11 Faith by £1.50

12 Both £40.80 so the same

Number 3EXT   Page 76

(ref. Foundation GCSE Maths 1–3 & 4–5 Unit 5)

1   Easy Bank (Easy Bank: £5408, Trickier Bank: £5407.50, Maybe Bank: £5404.50)

2   19

3   (a) correct   (b) $14 \div \frac{1}{5} = 14 \times 5 = 70$

4   1 : 4

5   £1200

6   (a) $M = kL$ so $20 = 5L$ so $k = 4$
    (b) 68
    (c) halved

7   not correct

8   £24

9   £158.48

10 (a) percentage should not be calculated using the new cost
    (b) £60

11 (a) 3200   (b) $2\frac{1}{2}$ hours saved

12 Reece Bank better by £11

PART TWO

Mixed 3A   Page 80

(ref. Foundation GCSE Maths 1–3 & 4–5 Units 1, 2, 3, 4, 5)

1   £97.60

2   Do not agree.   (a) $3^2 \times 3^2 = 3^4$
                    (b) $3^2 \times 2^3 = 9 \times 8 = 72$

3   $x = 120°$ so $3 \times 120° = 360°$ (no gaps)

4   $m = 11, n = 17$, difference = 6

5   2

6 WASHWELL £499.99 (DAWSONS £504, LECTROSTORE £510)

7 Both expressions equal $18n - 30$ so correct

8 $\frac{1}{5}$

9 First sketchpad is 50p (0.58 euros) more expensive

10 3, 1, 2 (10.5%, 10%, 9.5%)

11 122°

12 Two 1.5 litre cartons and one 2 litre carton: total cost £9.50

Mixed 3EXT   Page 84
(ref. Foundation GCSE Maths 1–3 & 4–5 Units 1, 2, 3, 4, 5)

1 £7.70

2 Declan is correct

3 9 : 5 : 8 or equivalent

4 Yes, sister gets £78.80

5 132°

6 Eva by £69

7 £3976

8 $x = 43°$ so both angles $= 162°$

9 (a) 2 litres blackcurrant and 8 litres lemonade
(b) 7.5 litres
(c) $\frac{1}{2}$

10 Borrow from the Paulton bank (£309 500 as opposed to £292 500)

11 the 500 ml cup

12 £98.25

Algebra 2A   Page 89
(ref. Foundation GCSE Maths 1–3 & 4–5 Unit 7)

1 21

2 Use table:

x	-4	-3	-2	-1	0	1	2	3
y	-3	-1	1	3	5	7	9	11

3 A, C correct. 3 should be subtracted not added in B.

4 £110

5 8 patterns and 6 matchsticks left over

6 B and D because both lines have gradient 5

7 Use table:

x	-4	-3	-2	-1	0	1	2	3	4
y	18	11	6	3	2	3	6	11	18

8 (a) at roughly 14:33 (or 14:34)
(b) 60 mph

9 gradient $= -2$ because line sloping downwards from left to right

10 Jordan is correct

11 (a) 13:45   (b) 11:45

12 (a) 23   (b) birthday 9

Algebra 2EXT   Page 95
(ref. Foundation GCSE Maths 1–3 & 4–5 Unit 7)

1 B–P, C–Q and A has no number line

2 not correct. He should have multiplied by 4 before adding c to both sides.

3 60 adults

4 $x = 5$

5 Yes, pattern 9 in the sequence

6 (a) $a = 1, b = 9$
(b) $y = x^2 - 10x + 9$ (i.e. $m = -10, n = 9$)

7 No. When $x = 2, y = 7$ on the line.

8 razor 90p and shaving brush £2.40

9 Yes. 6th term $= 6^2 - 3(6) = 18$

10 Yes. e.g. $y = 2x + 3$ so when $x = 5, y = 13$

11 (a) $0.75 \, \text{m/s}^2$ (b) acceleration

12 $(2, -1)$

Statistics 1A   Page 99

(ref. Foundation GCSE Maths 1–3 & 4–5 Unit 8)

1   $0.08 \times 175 = 14$

2   (a) $\mathscr{E}$

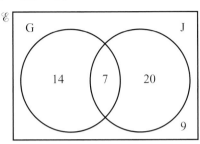

(b) $\frac{9}{50} = 0.18$

3   $\frac{2}{6} = \frac{1}{3}$

4   (a) $\frac{42}{300} = \frac{7}{50}$ (b) 70

5   Ability/experience levels are so different,etc.

6   (a) any suitable chart   (b) 56   (c) $\frac{11}{56}$

7   (a) 240; 72, 168; 48, 24, 84, 84   (b) $\frac{1}{3}$

8   (a) $\frac{1}{5}$ (b) 20

9   (a) No. Should be nearer 50% each for heads and tails.

(b) Kaylee has thrown the coin many more times than Adam and Megan so should provide more reliable results.

10 (a) 0.35   (b) 0.6   (c) once

11 Magpie Insurance Company by 9

12 $\frac{32}{100} = \frac{8}{25} = 0.32$

Statistics 1EXT   Page 104

(ref. Foundation GCSE Maths 1–3 & 4–5 Unit 8)

1   $n(\text{A}')$ greater by 2

2   any 2 independent events

3   (a) $\frac{68}{350} = \frac{34}{175}$ (b) $\frac{152}{350} = \frac{76}{175}$ (c) $\frac{198}{350} = \frac{99}{175}$

4   (a) $\frac{4}{16} = \frac{1}{4}$ (b) $\frac{3}{16}$

(c) equally likely $\left(\frac{2}{16} = \frac{1}{8}\right)$

5   (a) all probabilities $= \frac{1}{2}$ (b) $\frac{1}{4}$

6   $\frac{4}{25}$

7   (a) $\frac{28}{200} = \frac{7}{50} = 0.14$ (b) $\frac{112}{120} = \frac{14}{15}$

8   Each group of branches covers all possibilities so must add up to 1

9   $\frac{21}{32}$

10 $\frac{72}{380} = \frac{18}{95}$

12 6 times

Mixed 4A   Page 108

(ref. Foundation GCSE Maths 1–3 & 4–5 Units 1, 2, 3, 4, 5, 7, 8)

1   £556

2   $a^2 = -2 \times -2 = 4$ so $3a^2 = 3 \times 4 = 12$

3   motorcycle racing cheaper by £2.40

4   Larry (21), Jake (15), Josh (7)

5   480 g box

6   40°

7   4

8   sold 110 computers so new salary $= £18\,144$

9   A$(-3, 0)$, B$(-2, -2)$, C$(-3, -2)$

10 45

11 (a) A: $\frac{5}{8}$ and B: $\frac{3}{5}$

(b) A has greater proportion $\left(\frac{25}{40} \text{ compared to } \frac{24}{40}\right)$

12 £2030.40

Mixed 4EXT   Page 113

(ref. Foundation GCSE Maths 1–3 & 4–5 Units 1, 2, 3, 4, 5, 7, 8)

1   £41.88

2   both sides are equal to $4x^2 + 2x - 20$

3   (a) $\mathscr{E}$

(b) $\frac{11}{40}$ (c) $\frac{11}{21}$

4   Huo pays £300 more than Kevin

5   (a) $\overrightarrow{SQ} = \overrightarrow{SR} + \overrightarrow{RQ}$

(b) $\begin{pmatrix} 3 \\ 5 \end{pmatrix}$ (c) $\begin{pmatrix} -7 \\ 2 \end{pmatrix}$ (d) $\begin{pmatrix} -4 \\ 7 \end{pmatrix}$

6   £315.52

7   $x = 8.5$ so perimeter $= 169\,\text{cm}$

8   340 g tin is the best value

9   71°

10   240

11   0.4744

12   Zoe has the most money. Total $= £9262.20$

Geometry 2A   Page 117
(ref. Foundation GCSE Maths 1–3 & 4–5 Unit 9)

1   $16\,\text{cm}^2$

2   3:05 pm

3   5 cm

4   £425.75

5   Yes she can (total weight $= 7.475\,\text{kg}$)

6   9.8%

7   £71.88

8   3 hours 27 minutes

9   31.5 m

10   Three 2.5 l tins for a total of £55.50

11   Mackenzie's answer would be 10 miles per minute. She should have changed the minutes into hours.

12   £77.26

Geometry 2B   Page 122
(ref. Foundation GCSE Maths 1–3 & 4–5 Unit 9)

1   16:30

2   $84.1\,\text{cm}^2$

3   9 cm

4   5:35 pm

5   24.7 m

6   £468

7   $448\,\text{cm}^2$

8   £96.60

9   $38\,\text{m}^3$

10   correct. Car B (16 m/s) faster than car A (15 m/s)

11   (a) 1738   (b) 5 hours 39 minutes

12   12

Geometry 2EXT   Page 128
(ref. Foundation GCSE Maths 1–3 & 4–5 Unit 9)

1   12

2   gravel B cheaper by £20

3   (a) $31.6 \leqslant \text{weight} < 31.7$

    (b) each pencil sharpener could weigh up to 0.1 g more than 31.6 g so 700 sharpeners could weigh up to $700 \times 0.1\,\text{g} = 70\,\text{g}$ more.

4   £1500 (6 m $\times$ 8 m and 6 m $\times$ 2 m)

5   90.9%

7   $(6.2 \times 200 + 7.8 \times 300) \div 500 = 7.16\,\text{g/cm}^3$

8   20

9   (a) $1\,\text{m}^3 = 1\,\text{m} \times 1\,\text{m} \times 1\,\text{m} = 100\,\text{cm} \times 100\,\text{cm} \times 100\,\text{cm} = 1\,000\,000\,\text{cm}^3$

    (b) $5\,000\,000\,\text{cm}^3$

10   £179.20

11   stand on triangular face (least area $96\,\text{cm}^2$ compared to $600\,\text{cm}^2$, $360\,\text{cm}^2$ and $480\,\text{cm}^2$)

12   (b) 4 m $\times$ 6 m $\times$ 9 m

Statistics 2A   Page 133
(ref. Foundation GCSE Maths 1–3 & 4–5 Unit 10)

1   any suitable comparison (Blake: median $= 52$, range $= 70$ and Stella: median $= 40$, range $= 34$)

2   (a) and (b) 1, 4, 10 or 2, 4, 9 or 3, 4, 8 or 4, 4, 7

3   43

4   any suitable question

5   17 or 41

6   No money left over. Juan spends exactly £170.

7   Evie is correct (Hatton tennis 20, Whitstone tennis 18)

8   18

9   2.975

10   height and shoe size

11 any suitable diagram or chart

12 (a) frequency: 8, 20, 13, 7, 2

   (b) 75   (c) 1.5

Statistics 2B   Page 139

(ref. Foundation GCSE Maths 1–3 & 4–5 Unit 10)

1 5 and 9

2 any suitable diagram or chart

3 51

4 Not correct. Do not know how many people were asked, etc.

5 (b) any suitable comments

6 28

7 any suitable description

8 (a) 6.8

   (b) lower because 6 is lower than the mean 6.8

9 any suitable diagram or chart

10 (a) any suitable chart

    (b) $70 \leqslant W < 80$

    (c) 75 kg

    (d) mean weight increases because 80 kg > old mean of 75 kg

11 (a) Frequency: 3, 3, 1, 2, 4, 3

    (b) mode = 21 cm, median = 20 cm, range = 5 cm

    (c) Lengths in box A are generally greater than the lengths in box B (use an average). Lengths in box A are less spread out than the lengths in box B (use of range).

12 (a) 17   (b) 17   (c) 23   (d) 18

    (e) median stays the same (one value below old median and one value above old median)

Statistics 2EXT   Page 145

(ref. Foundation GCSE Maths 1–3 & 4–5 Unit 10)

1 Yes, they collected £622

2 Madeley High School by 5

3 (b) positive correlation

   (c) depends on line of best fit

   (d) not reliable, outside the data range, would give a negative shoe size

4 Labour 108°, UKIP 48°, Conservative 144°, Lib Dem 60°

5 median larger by 0.4 (mean = 3.6, median = 4)

6 (a) Each member has an equal probability of being chosen.

   (b) No. Natalia's method should but Anton's approach is not fair (paper not of equal size, pieces stick together so not properly mixed up)

7 Yes, assuming a Winter decline in sales

8 any suitable comparison
   (Forest United: mean = 21.65, range = 5
   Castle Rangers: mean = 25.8, range = 14)

9 7

10 70 kg

11 (a) around 10, depending on line of best fit

    (b) 1 drink, 30°C max. temp.

    (c) outside the data range (would actually get a negative number of drinks)

12 (a) 8   (b) 73

Mixed 5A   Page 152

(ref. Foundation GCSE Maths 1–3 & 4–5 Units 1–5, 7–10)

1 £20

2 p and q = 16 and 25 (m = 40, n = 41)

3 £74.94

4 7

5 Lucy has not taken out 3 with her common factor so the answer should be $12a(3a - b)$

6 (a) 35   (b) Wednesday   (d) 40

7 £2520

8 (b) 8 cm

9 48.5%

10 $\frac{10}{80} = \frac{1}{8}$

11 any suitable comparison (snail: median = 91 s, range = 27 s)

12 Mrs Williams: 16p per unit, Mr Harris: 15p per unit. Cotswold Electric Company is cheaper.

Mixed 5EXT Page 157

(ref. Foundation GCSE Maths 1–3 & 4–5 Units 1–5, 7–10)

1 4 days

2 £99.83

3 Angles in a pentagon add up to 540° (3 triangles), etc.

4 $2^0 \div 2^4 = 2^{0-4} = 2^{-4}$ and $2^0 \div 2^4 = 1 \div 2^4 = \dfrac{1}{2^4}$

5 168 miles

6 £45

7 signs wrong way round when factorising.
   $x = 3$ so perimeter $= 18$ cm

8 $\dfrac{53}{595}$

9 20% increase

10 $\overrightarrow{QR} = 2\mathbf{b} - \mathbf{a}$ so $\overrightarrow{QX} = \frac{1}{3}\overrightarrow{QR} = \frac{1}{3}(2\mathbf{b} - \mathbf{a})$
    $= \frac{2}{3}\mathbf{b} - \frac{1}{3}\mathbf{a}$

11 Asha is correct ($2\pi r^2 + $ base πr^2)

12 triangle ABC: 60°, 70°, 50° and triangle PQR:
    40°, 55°, 85°

Geometry 3A Page 162

(ref. Foundation GCSE Maths 1–3 & 4–5 Unit 11)

1 Not correct. Final cross should be at (4, 2)

2 6 cm : 1800 cm = 1 : 300

3 115°

4 C is correct

5 9

6 Should be 130°. Mariana probably used the wrong scale on the protractor.

7 8 mm

8 (a) anti-clockwise   (b) 178°

9 The angles are too large for a triangle or two of the sides would never meet, etc.

10 220°

11 trapezium

12 3400 cm³

Geometry 3EXT Page 167

(ref. Foundation GCSE Maths 1–3 & 4–5 Unit 11)

1 24 cm²

2 28.6 cm

3 4.29 m

4 1050 m³

5 28.5 mins

6 Yes (diagonal = 23.26 cm)

7 302°

8 33.4 cm

9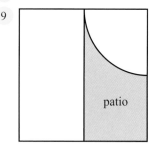
   patio

10 £1428.90

11 diagonals of a rhombus bisect each other and cross at right angles

12 31.8 m

Mixed 6A Page 172

(ref. Foundation GCSE Maths 1–3 & 4–5 Units 1–5, 7–11)

1 £14.40

2 1 kg and 2 kg, total cost £6.10

3 any suitable chart or diagram

4 $Q\hat{P}R = 60°$ (angles on a straight line add up to 180°), $P\hat{R}Q = 60°$ (alternate angles are equal) so $P\hat{Q}R = 60°$ (angles in a triangle add up to 180°). All angles equal so triangle PQR is equilateral.

5 12

6 (a) 39   (b) 76
   (c) James median = 57, James range = 53.
       Any suitable comparisons between the medians and ranges for Kevin and James.

7 $a = 4$

8   4 rolls, total cost £74

9   16:47

10 4 cm

11 £62.52

12 305°

Mixed 6B   Page 178

(ref. Foundation GCSE Maths 1–3 & 4–5 Units 1–5, 7–11)

1   £108

2   any suitable diagram or chart

3   '28 tablet' box is the best value

4   (a) can only have probabilities $0.01 = \frac{1}{100}$ and $0.49 = \frac{49}{100}$ if there are at least 100 balls in total.

    (b) 147

5   (a) $\frac{1}{10}$

    (b) $1 \div 0.1 = 10$ so $6 \div 0.1 = 60$

    (c) 0.2 is double 0.1 so $6 \div 0.2$ will be half of $6 \div 0.1$, i.e. 30

6   77.4%

7   earliest bus: 1835; arrives home at 1926

8   rotation 180° about (0, 0)

9   Carl, cheaper by £45

10 Not correct. 7th term of sequence A is 51. 8th term of sequence B is 45 (9th term = 51)

11 any suitable comparison (city: mean = 5.05, range = 10)

12 11

Mixed 6C   Page 184

(ref. Foundation GCSE Maths 1–3 & 4–5 Units 1–5, 7–11)

1   3

2   4915 cm²

3   78°

4   (a) $x^3 + 3x^2$ (b) 112 cm²

5   60 mph

6   Barcelona, Nice, Venice

7   £1862 cm²

8   (a) 2   (b) $\frac{8}{13}$

9   any suitable chart

10 (a) £502.80   (b) Yes, he saved £339.36

11 (c) area of rectangle = 28 square units

12 (a) 57p   (b) 58p

Mixed 6EXT   Page 190

(ref. Foundation GCSE Maths 1–3 & 4–5 Units 1–5, 7–11)

1   100

2   (a) negative correlation

    (b) depends on line of best fit

    (c) the given data is only in the 1–5 year age range

3   27 cm

4   should be $x^2 + 8x + 16 + 12x + 6 = x^2 + 20x + 22$

5   8.5 km on a bearing of 339.4°

6   $2x$

7   30 boxes

8   $4x + 32$

9   $\frac{3}{7}$

10 210 points

11 during the 7th year

12 11.9%

Question Index 14(6) means Page 14 Question 6